I ♥ Good Food

RECIPES DEVELOPED AND WRITTEN IN ASSOCIATION WITH
ORLA BRODERICK

PHOTOGRAPHER: NEIL MACDOUGALD
FOOD STYLIST: ANN KENNY

IRISH HEART
FOUNDATION
Fighting Heart Disease & Stroke

POOLBEG

Published 2011
Poolbeg Press Ltd.
123 Grange Hill, Baldoyle,
Dublin 13, Ireland
Email: poolbeg@poolbeg.com

1

A catalogue record for this book is available from the British Library.

ISBN 978-1-84223-487-7

Photography by Neil Macdougald
Book design and typesetting by Steven and Patricia Hope

Printed by GraficasCems · Spain

www.poolbeg.com

contents

Main Course: Pork

Main Course: Poultry

Main Course: Beef

Desserts   177

Breads and Cakes   211

acknowledgements

A number of people have been invaluable in the development of this cookbook. The recipes were developed and written in association with Orla Broderick, whose energy, enthusiasm and inspired knowledge of food has kept our mouths watering for many months. Orla, the Chairperson of the Irish Food Writers' Guild, was also the meticulous tester of our recipes, ensuring a high standard throughout the cookbook.

Sincere thanks to photographer Neil Macdougald and food stylist Ann Kenny for their commitment and dedication to creating beautiful photography.

Thank you to all the celebrities, chefs and cookery writers who generously contributed recipes to the cookbook.

All recipes were nutritionally analysed by Dr Patricia Heavey and Orla McMahon from the National Nutrition Surveillance Centre at University College Dublin, who worked in a professional and timely manner to ensure we met our deadlines.

Several of the staff in the Irish Heart Foundation played a key role in developing the cookbook. Thanks to Sharon Daly for her management of the project and Janis Morrissey, dietitian, who provided excellent input at all stages of the book. A big thanks to Mairéad O'Callaghan for such efficient administration. The contributions of Maureen Mulvihill and Caroline Cullen were a great asset.

The Irish Heart Foundation also acknowledges the enthusiasm and support we have received from Poolbeg Press Limited. The support of such an experienced and established publisher has been invaluable throughout the development of this book.

Finally, we'd like to give full credit to Irish Heart Foundation staff member, Chitra Howie, for the inspired cookbook title!

foreword

Quite simply, we all love good food. It's also true, to a certain extent, that we are what we eat, but with the many food messages out there it's often difficult to choose food that's both delicious and good for you. On the island of Ireland we are fortunate enough to have an abundance of fresh, natural food available to us and, with a little help and guidance, we can all enjoy this delicious food while maintaining a nutritious, balanced and heart-healthy diet.

The Irish Heart Foundation cookbook is designed to help us do just that. We've included some old-time favourites, a few modern selections, and signature dishes from some familiar personalities and establishments. You'll find mouth-watering dishes for a variety of occasions from family dinners, to 'on the go' meals, to something a little different for a night of entertaining. All this while sticking to our goal for a happy heart – enjoy food that is heart-healthy and rich in taste.

We hope that you enjoy the book, whether you're an experienced cook or an eager beginner.

Bon appétit!

Michael P. O'Shea

Michael O'Shea
Chief Executive
Irish Heart Foundation

IRISH HEART
FOUNDATION
Fighting Heart Disease & Stroke

healthy eating –
good for your heart

To get the most out of life, it is important to take care of our bodies and to think about the food we eat. About one third of premature deaths from heart disease are due to an unhealthy diet. So what we eat has a big impact on our chances of developing heart disease and stroke.

In addition to the wonderful heart-healthy recipes, you will find information throughout this book on the relationship between the foods we eat and heart health or, more importantly, how you can lower your risk of heart disease and stroke.

It is the overall daily and weekly balance of foods that determines whether an eating plan is healthy or not.

Variety is the spice of life!

The cornerstone of healthy eating is choosing a wide variety of foods and getting a balance of essential nutrients without getting too much of any one nutrient, such as fat or sugar.

It is more difficult to have a healthy diet if you eat only a limited number of foods, particularly if those foods are high in fat and low in fibre. The wider the variety of foods you eat, the more likely you are to get all the nutrients needed.

Making small changes to your eating habits over time can make a huge difference to your health. Positive lifestyle changes are the key to preventing a heart attack or stroke.

To eat a wide variety of foods, follow the Food Pyramid *(see page 230).*

Notes on nutritional analysis

All recipes have been analysed by the National Nutritional Surveillance Centre, UCD, Dublin using a recognised nutritional analysis computer software program. Where serving size for a recipe states a range of portions, the analysis refers to the greater number, for example if a recipe serves 4-6, the analysis refers to 6 portions. Where serving suggestions are stated the nutritional analysis also includes these foods.

For further information and advice on heart health and the work of the Irish Heart Foundation visit www.irishheart.ie. If you have a query or concern in relation to heart health, or cardiovascular diseases such as heart disease or stroke, call the Heart and Stroke Helpline on 1890 432 787.

Starters

antipasti platter with hummus and parma ham

With a little clever shopping you can have this stunning platter on the table in less than ten minutes! This recipe uses Peppadew, which are mild whole sweet peppers and are well worth seeking out (but halved cherry tomatoes would also work well). They come in jars and are normally kept beside the olives in large supermarkets. Look out for light tahini paste in the health food section of most large supermarkets, but you'll always find it in health food shops. Once opened, it keeps well in the fridge.

Preparation time: 10 minutes • **Cooking time:** none • *Serves 4-6*

what you need

For the platter
4 slices Parma ham
100g (4oz) Peppadew, drained
(see introduction)
100g (4oz) marinated black olives,
drained
handful of wild rocket

For the dressing
1 teaspoon extra-virgin olive oil
½ teaspoon balsamic vinegar

For the hummus
100g (4oz) tinned chickpeas, drained
and rinsed
1 small garlic clove, chopped
1 tablespoon light tahini (optional) –
(see introduction)
squeeze of fresh lemon juice
pinch of cayenne pepper
freshly ground black pepper

crisp Italian flatbreads, to serve

what you do

To make the hummus, place the chickpeas in a food processor with the garlic, tahini (if using), the lemon juice and cayenne pepper, putting aside a little cayenne pepper to garnish. Add two tablespoons of water and season lightly with black pepper, then blend to a smooth paste. Spoon into a serving bowl.

Set the bowl of hummus on a large platter. Arrange the slices of Parma ham on the platter with loose mounds of the Peppadew and olives. Tip the rocket into a bowl and dress lightly with the extra-virgin olive oil and balsamic vinegar. Pile on to the platter with a stack of the crisp Italian flatbreads to serve.

typical nutritional content – *per portion*			
Energy Kcal (Calories)	259	Salt (g)	2.2
Fat (g)	9.7	Sugars (g)	5.3
of which saturates (g)	1.7		

spicy crunchy chicken salad in lettuce cups

★ *RECIPE BY* Canice Sharkey Isaac's Restaurant *Cork*

This has always been a really popular dish in the restaurant – simple, with lovely tastes and textures. The lettuce and peanuts give a wonderful crunch to the dish.

Preparation time: 15 mins + 15 mins cooling • **Cooking time:** 15 mins • *Serves 6*

what you need

6 tablespoons freshly squeezed lime juice
50g (2oz) caster sugar
3 tablespoons Thai fish sauce (nam pla)
2 tablespoons chilli paste (from a jar or tube)
2 tablespoons vegetable oil
2.5cm (1in) piece root ginger, peeled and minced
2 garlic cloves, minced (or very finely chopped/crushed)
450g (1lb) minced chicken or skinless chicken fillets, finely chopped
4 spring onions, thinly sliced

1 medium carrot, grated
100g (4oz) water chestnuts (from a can), finely chopped
2 tablespoons fresh mint, chopped
2 tablespoons fresh coriander, chopped
2 heads Little Gem lettuce (or use another crisp lettuce such as cos)
50g (2oz) unsalted roasted peanuts, chopped
freshly ground black pepper
4 lime wedges, to garnish

what you do

Whisk together the lime juice, sugar, fish sauce and chilli paste in a small bowl until the sugar has dissolved.

Heat the oil in a large frying-pan over a medium heat. Add the ginger and garlic and stir-fry for about 20 seconds. Add the chicken and a little pepper, and stir-fry for 3-4 minutes or until the chicken is tender and cooked through, breaking up any lumps with the back of a wooden spoon.

Stir the spring onions into the chicken with the carrot and water chestnuts and allow to just warm through. Transfer to a bowl and leave to cool. Stir the mint and coriander into the lime-juice dressing and pour over the chicken.

Strip any damaged leaves from the lettuce and then separate into leaves before washing and drying. Arrange the lettuce leaves on a platter and fill each with some of the chicken salad, then sprinkle the peanuts on top. Garnish with the lime wedges to serve.

typical nutritional content – *per portion*			
Energy Kcal (Calories)	244	Salt (g)	1.2
Fat (g)	11.8	Sugars (g)	11.2
of which saturates (g)	1.2		

fresh and smoked salmon tartare with horseradish

★ RECIPE BY Mark Bodie PEARL BRASSERIE *Upper Merrion Street, Dublin 2*

This dish has proved immensely successful for us and I think it is because it's the sort of light dish that everybody wants to eat these days. It is fantastic, particularly when made with good-quality smoked salmon and very fresh salmon fillets.

Preparation time: 15 minutes • **Cooking time:** none • *Serves 6*

what you need

For the horseradish dressing
1 tablespoon mascarpone cheese
½ tablespoon maple syrup
½ tablespoon sherry vinegar
½ tablespoon creamed horseradish
(from a jar)
freshly ground black pepper

For the salmon
275g (10oz) fresh salmon, skinned and boned
150g (5oz) smoked salmon slices

1 crisp eating apple, peeled, cored and diced
1 red onion, diced
1 tomato, peeled, seeded and diced
1 celery stick, diced
1 teaspoon each of fresh chives (snipped into little pieces) and dill, plus extra to garnish
a little fresh lemon juice
a drop of Tabasco sauce
a little olive oil

what you do

To make the horseradish dressing, place the mascarpone cheese in a bowl and whisk in the maple syrup, sherry vinegar and horseradish. Season with freshly ground black pepper and leave to rest for 1 hour.

Meanwhile, prepare the salmon. Dice the fresh and smoked salmon as small as possible and mix in a bowl. Fold in the apple, red onion, tomato, celery and herbs. Season to your liking with lemon juice, Tabasco, pepper and olive oil. Don't be tempted to use salt as the smoked salmon will be salty enough.

Spoon the salmon mixture into rounds in the centre of plates and drizzle the dressing around it. Garnish with the herbs and serve at once.

typical nutritional content – *per portion*			
Energy Kcal (Calories)	155	Salt (g)	1.3
Fat (g)	8.4	Sugars (g)	3.3
of which saturates (g)	2.1		

garlic yoghurt cheese with crudités

This wonderful recipe takes some plain yoghurt and overnight turns it into a delightful well-flavoured cheese. It also works well with goats' yoghurt – it just has a more pronounced flavour. If you don't have time to let the flavoured yoghurt sit overnight in the fridge, it also tastes great as a dip.

Preparation time: 15 mins + drain 4 hrs, chill overnight • **Cooking time:** none • *Serves 4*

what you need

450ml (¾ pint) low-fat thick natural yoghurt
1 large garlic clove, crushed
3 tablespoons fresh mixed herbs (such as chives, flat-leaf parsley, dill and basil), chopped

450g (1lb) mixed bite-size crudités, such as broccoli florets, radishes, carrot batons and celery sticks
a little salt and freshly ground black pepper
muslin (a brand new, clean J Cloth or other form of porous cloth will do)

what you do

Combine the yoghurt, garlic and herbs in a bowl. Season lightly with a little salt and pepper to taste and mix until well combined. Place a double layer of muslin (or cloth) in a sieve and spoon in the mixture.

Place the sieve over a bowl and leave to drain in a cool place for 4 hours, then chill overnight. This gives the cheese time to settle and for all of the excess moisture to drain off, leaving behind a lovely soft cheese.

When ready to serve, unwrap the flavoured cheese and serve on a large plate with a selection of crudités.

typical nutritional content – *per portion*			
Energy Kcal (Calories)	92	Salt (g)	0.3
Fat (g)	1.4	Sugars (g)	12.3
of which saturates (g)	0.7		

warm goats' cheese and mango salad

★ RECIPE BY Sinéad Desmond Television Presenter

This has to be one of my all-time favourite dishes, perfect for entertaining. It is stunning and simple – need I say more? Oh, and it tastes great too.

Preparation time: 10 minutes • **Cooking time:** 10 minutes • *Serves 4*

what you need

4 teaspoons pine nuts
50g (2oz) mixed salad leaves (such as spinach, watercress and rocket)
1 small ripe mango
1 tablespoon extra-virgin olive oil

a little fresh lemon juice
4 slices of goats' cheese with rind, each about 2.5cm (1in) thick
4 fresh thyme sprigs
freshly ground black pepper

what you do

Preheat the oven to 200°C/400°F/Gas Mark 6.

Place the salad leaves in a bowl. Place the pine nuts in a small baking tin and cook for about 5 minutes in the oven until toasted. Set aside to cool.

Peel the mango and then thinly slice, discarding the stone. Fold into the salad leaves and then lightly dress with olive oil and lemon juice. Season with pepper.

Arrange the goats' cheese on a baking tray lined with parchment paper and place in the oven for 3-4 minutes to just warm through.

Preheat the grill and quickly grill the goats' cheese so the top begins to melt.

Divide the salad leaves and mango mixture between plates and scatter the toasted pine nuts over. Arrange the goats' cheese on top. Garnish with the thyme sprigs and serve at once.

typical nutritional content – *per portion*			
Energy Kcal (Calories)	176	Salt (g)	0.5
Fat (g)	14.0	Sugars (g)	5.4
of which saturates (g)	6.0		

roasted red peppers with anchovies

These make a fantastic starter or lovely side dish for a barbecue. Although the stalks of the peppers are not edible they do look attractive and help the peppers keep their shape. Omit the anchovies if you are not keen on them or want to serve this to vegetarians. Or try using capers instead.

Preparation time: 10 minutes • Cooking time: 1 hour • *Serves 4*

what you need

4 large red peppers
4 ripe tomatoes
4 anchovy fillets, drained
2 garlic cloves, finely chopped

4 teaspoons olive oil
handful fresh small basil leaves
freshly ground black pepper

what you do

Preheat the oven to 180°C/350°F/Gas Mark 4.

Cut the peppers in half, slicing through the stalks so that there is half a stalk left on each half-pepper. Remove the seeds. Arrange the pepper halves open side up on a non-stick baking tin.

Place the tomatoes in a bowl and cover with boiling water. Leave for 1 minute, then drain and peel the skins off. Cut into quarters and place two quarters into each pepper half. Using scissors, snip the anchovy fillets over the peppers and scatter the garlic on top.

Lightly season the filled pepper halves with pepper and drizzle the olive oil over them. Roast for 50 minutes to 1 hour until the peppers are completely tender and lightly charred around the edges.

Transfer the peppers to plates and spoon all of the cooking juices over them. Scatter the basil leaves over and serve warm or at room temperature.

typical nutritional content – *per portion*			
Energy Kcal (Calories)	100	Salt (g)	0.3
Fat (g)	4.2	Sugars (g)	12.4
of which saturates (g)	0.7		

watermelon and feta salad

★ *RECIPE BY* Denis Cotter CAFE PARADISO *16 Lancaster Quay, Cork*

This recipe also works with Galia or honeydew melon if watermelon is not in season. Tried once, it will become a regular feature at your summer table.

Preparation time: 10 minutes • **Cooking time:** 10 minutes • *Serves 4*

what you need

2 tablespoons pumpkin seeds
1 tablespoon green peppercorns, rinsed and drained if in brine
1kg (2¼lb) watermelon, seeded and flesh cut into medium-sized chunks (rind discarded)

120g (4½oz) feta cheese
finely grated rind and juice of 2 limes
2 tablespoons olive oil

what you do

Preheat the oven to 180°C/350°F/Gas Mark 4.

Toast the pumpkin seeds in a small baking dish for 5-6 minutes or until lightly browned. Crack the peppercorns gently between your fingers or with the flat of a knife. Chop the feta into small cubes and place in a bowl with the watermelon and the pumpkin seeds. Add the lime rind and juice with the olive oil and toss gently to combine. Pile a mound of the watermelon and feta salad onto each plate. Scatter the green peppercorns over and serve chilled or at room temperature.

typical nutritional content – *per portion*			
Energy Kcal (Calories)	248	Salt (g)	1.3
Fat (g)	16.0	Sugars (g)	18.4
of which saturates (g)	5.7		

buffalo mozzarella with vine tomatoes and basil

Buffalo mozzarella makes a delicious occasional starter – keep to the amounts used here and serve it with plenty of vine tomatoes. If you want to make this recipe even lower in fat then just use a drizzle of balsamic vinegar instead of the basil and parsley dressing. You can also use the dressing with pasta or on French bread slices – it's delicious and lower in fat than traditional pesto.

Preparation time: 10 minutes • **Cooking time:** none • *Serves 4-6*

what you need

For the salad
150g (5oz) packet buffalo mozzarella cheese, thinly sliced
450g (1lb) vine tomatoes, thinly sliced
handful fresh basil leaves

For the basil and parsley dressing
1 tablespoon fresh basil, chopped
1 tablespoon fresh flat-leaf parsley, chopped

1 teaspoon balsamic vinegar
1 garlic clove, crushed
good pinch of dried chilli (optional)
3 tablespoons olive oil
freshly ground black pepper

ciabatta or wholemeal brown crusty bread, to serve

what you do

To make the dressing, place the basil and parsley in a bowl with the balsamic vinegar, garlic and dried chilli (if using) and then stir in the olive oil. Season lightly with black pepper.

To prepare the salad, arrange the slices of tomatoes on a large platter or plate. Season the tomatoes with freshly ground black pepper. Tear the basil leaves into small pieces and scatter over the tomatoes and then arrange the buffalo mozzarella in an overlapping layer down the centre.

Lightly drizzle the dressing over and serve straight to the table with a separate basket of bread.

typical nutritional content – *per portion*			
Energy Kcal (Calories)	381	Salt (g)	0.9
Fat (g)	12.6	Sugars (g)	3.7
of which saturates (g)	4.6		

beetroot, red onion and feta salad with walnuts

★ *RECIPE BY* Garrett Byrne CAMPAGNE *The Arches, 5 Gashouse Lane, Kilkenny*

This beetroot would also be wonderful served with some orange segments, or alongside smoked mackerel with a dollop of horseradish dressing.

Preparation time: 10 mins • **Cooking time:** 50 mins + 1 hr marinating • *Serves 4*

what you need

4 medium beetroot, trimmed and
scrubbed clean
100ml (3.5fl oz) red wine vinegar
100g (4oz) sugar
2 red onions, cut into thin rounds
100g (4oz) feta cheese

20 walnuts, cracked and shelled
(as fresh as possible)
50g (2oz) mixed baby salad leaves
1-2 tablespoons walnut oil
freshly ground black pepper

what you do

Place the beetroot in a pan of water and bring to the boil, then reduce the heat and simmer for about 45 minutes until just tender.

Meanwhile, place the red wine vinegar and sugar in a pan and bring to the boil, then remove from the heat and pour over the red onions. Leave to stand for at least 1 hour to allow the flavours to develop, stirring occasionally.

Drain the beetroot and, when just cool enough to handle but still warm, quickly peel them and thinly slice. Place in a bowl and add the remaining tablespoons of the vinegar-sugar mixture. Leave to stand for at least one hour.

Preheat the oven to 180°C/350°F/Gas Mark 4.

Place the walnuts in a small roasting tin and roast for 6-8 minutes until toasted and golden brown. Remove from the oven, place in a clean tea towel and then wrap up and rub together to remove the skins.

Drain the marinated beetroot slices and arrange in a circle in a slightly overlapping layer on each serving plate. Season with pepper. Drain the red onion rings and scatter over the beetroot. Crumble the feta cheese on top.

Place the salad leaves in a bowl, season with pepper and then toss with the roasted walnuts and 1-2 tablespoons of walnut oil, enough to just barely coat the leaves.

Arrange the dressed leaves and nuts loosely on top of the beetroot salads to serve. This dish is best served at room temperature.

typical nutritional content – *per portion*			
Energy Kcal (Calories)	344	Salt (g)	1.0
Fat (g)	20.7	Sugars (g)	31.9
of which saturates (g)	4.7		

NOTE: The marinade ingredients are included in the nutritional analysis (as is the case with all other recipes) but much of the marinade is drained away during preparation. Therefore the consumed nutritional measures will be less than stated above.

chinese-style steamed scallops in the shell

★ *RECIPE BY* Tony Tormey *Actor,* FAIR CITY

This is my version of a classic Chinese dish that I've often enjoyed whilst eating out. You will need to go to a good fishmonger to get the scallops but for me they are worth the effort every time. Scallop shells make excellent containers for seafood and can look very dramatic; look out for them in fishmongers' but, of course, they are not necessary to make this dish.

Preparation time: 5 minutes • **Cooking time:** 5 minutes • *Serves 4*

what you need

20 large scallops, well trimmed
20 scallop shells (optional –
see introduction)
1 teaspoon fresh root ginger,
finely chopped
4 teaspoons dark soy sauce

2 teaspoons toasted sesame oil
1 tablespoon fresh coriander,
roughly torn
2 spring onions, very thinly sliced

what you do

Pour 2.5cm (1in) of water into the base of a pan with a steamer attachment and bring it to the boil.

Arrange the scallops on the steamer and sprinkle the ginger over. Reduce the heat to medium, then cover with a lid and cook for 2-3 minutes until just cooked through and tender.

Lift the scallops onto shells that have been warmed in the oven (if using) and then arrange on platters. Quickly drizzle the soy sauce and toasted sesame oil over. Scatter the coriander and spring onions over and serve immediately.

typical nutritional content – *per portion*			
Energy Kcal (Calories)	100	Salt (g)	1.2
Fat (g)	3.8	Sugars (g)	0.6
of which saturates (g)	0.7		

crunchy thai tofu salad

★ RECIPE BY Rosanna Davison *Model and former Miss Ireland*

This is a firm favourite in my house and always seems to go down well even for committed meat-eaters. If you are short of time there is now a wide variety of prepared stir-fry vegetables available in the chilled section of large supermarkets. Although some supermarkets now stock tofu, you may have to make a special trip to a health food store depending on where you live.

Preparation time: 10 mins + 15 mins marinating • **Cooking time:** 10 mins • *Serves 4*

what you need

250g (9oz) packet tofu
4 tablespoons Thai sweet chilli dipping sauce
1 tablespoon dark soy sauce, plus extra to serve
1 tablespoon sesame oil
1 teaspoon root ginger, freshly grated
1 small garlic clove, crushed
1 lemongrass stick, finely minced, with tough stalk removed

50g (2oz) bean sprouts
1 red pepper, seeded and very thinly sliced
1 yellow pepper, seeded and very thinly sliced
50g (2oz) small button mushrooms, thinly sliced
2 spring onions, finely chopped
25g (1oz) unsalted roasted peanuts, roughly chopped

what you do

Drain the tofu, then pat dry with kitchen paper and cut into chunky bite-size pieces. Put into a bowl and then stir in two tablespoons of the Thai sweet chilli dipping sauce and the dark soy sauce. Toss together and set aside to marinate for 15 minutes to allow the flavours to penetrate the tofu.

Heat the sesame oil in a wok or large frying-pan over a medium-high heat. When hot, add the tofu and cook for 3-4 minutes, turning halfway, until golden and sticky. Set aside in a large bowl to cool slightly. Then fold in the ginger, garlic and lemongrass with the rest of the sweet chilli sauce. Add the bean sprouts, red and yellow peppers, mushrooms and spring onions and gently stir until nicely combined.

Arrange the tofu salad on plates and scatter the peanuts over to serve. Serve with the extra dark soy sauce, to drizzle over.

typical nutritional content – *per portion*			
Energy Kcal (Calories)	268	Salt (g)	1.8
Fat (g)	17.2	Sugars (g)	8.8
of which saturates (g)	1.0		

smoked mackerel pâté

This pâté is great as a starter or for serving on canapés when entertaining. It also is a quick and easy snack served on crackers or hot toast. Look out for cold smoked mackerel, which can be more difficult to find, but has a wonderful pale golden colour and delicate flavour.

Preparation time: 10 minutes • Cooking time: none • *Serves 6-8*

what you need

275g (10oz) smoked mackerel fillets
2 spring onions, very finely sliced
150g (5oz) low-fat or light cream cheese or Quark (semi-skimmed-milk soft cheese)
150g (5oz) half-fat crème fraîche
2 tablespoons creamed horseradish

dash of Tabasco sauce
juice of ½ lemon
freshly ground black pepper

selection of granary crackers and celery sticks, to serve

what you do

Remove the skin from the mackerel fillets and discard any bones, then break up the flesh into a bowl. Add the spring onions, low-fat/light cream cheese or Quark, crème fraîche, horseradish, Tabasco and lemon juice. Mix thoroughly until well combined. Season lightly with pepper and transfer to a serving bowl.

Place the bowl of smoked mackerel pâté on a platter and add a selection of granary crackers and celery sticks to serve.

typical nutritional content – *per portion*			
Energy Kcal (Calories)	201	Salt (g)	0.9
Fat (g)	14.7	Sugars (g)	2.1
of which saturates (g)	4.5		

garlic toast with aubergine and tahini (baba ghanoush)

This delicious dish can be served as a light lunch in the garden to bring back memories of Mediterranean holidays. It also makes a very good starter served before a long lazy Sunday lunch. Tahini paste is available in the health food section of most large supermarkets or in health food shops.

Preparation time: 10 minutes • Cooking time: 50 minutes • *Serves 4-6*

what you need

For the baba ghanoush
1 large aubergine
juice of 1 lemon
3 tablespoons light tahini paste
(see introduction)
2 large garlic cloves, crushed
5 tablespoons Greek-style yoghurt
2 tablespoons fresh flat-leaf parsley,
chopped
pinch of ground cumin
freshly ground black pepper

For the garlic toasts
1 ciabatta or wholemeal crusty
bread loaf
1 large garlic clove, peeled
freshly ground black pepper

what you do

Depending on how you want to cook the aubergine, either preheat the grill to hot or the oven to 200°C/400°F/Gas Mark 6.

Pierce the aubergine in a few places with the point of a knife or a fork and cook under the grill, turning frequently, until the skin has blackened and the aubergine is soft. Alternatively, bake in a small roasting tin for about 45 minutes, depending on the size of the aubergine. Peel off the skin while still hot and place the flesh in a bowl.

Mash the warm aubergine flesh to a purée, using a potato-masher or fork. Beat in the lemon juice, tahini paste and garlic. Set aside until cool and then fold in the yoghurt. Season lightly with pepper and add the cumin with most of the parsley, stirring to combine.

To prepare the garlic toast, preheat the grill or a griddle pan. Cut the ciabatta or loaf into 2.5cm (1in) slices on a slight diagonal – you should get at least 8-10 slices in total. Cook for a few minutes on each side until nicely toasted and, if using a griddle pan, lightly charred. Cut the garlic clove in half and use to rub over one side of each piece of toast.

Spread the garlic toast with the baba ghanoush and scatter the rest of the parsley on top. Arrange on plates and serve while the toast is still warm.

typical nutritional content – *per portion*			
Energy Kcal (Calories)	289	Salt (g)	0.7
Fat (g)	16.2	Sugars (g)	3.8
of which saturates (g)	3.9		

Soups

carrot and ginger soup

This is the perfect soup to make if you haven't got much in the house but feel like something comforting. It's extremely easy to prepare, making it just the thing for a leisurely lunch or a late-night supper.

Preparation time: 20 minutes • **Cooking time:** 25 minutes • *Serves 6*

what you need

1 tablespoon olive oil
1 large onion, finely grated
2.5cm (1in) fresh root ginger, peeled and finely grated
675g (1½lb) carrots, finely chopped
1 tablespoon clear honey
1 tablespoon fresh lemon juice

900ml (1½ pints) vegetable stock
2 tablespoons half-fat crème fraîche
freshly ground black pepper
2 teaspoons fresh chives, snipped into little pieces

what you do

Heat the olive oil in a large pan. Add the onion and ginger and cook over a low heat for 1 minute until just beginning to soften, stirring.

Add the carrots to the onion and ginger mixture with the honey and lemon juice. Stir to combine and pour in the stock. Bring to the boil, then reduce the heat and simmer for 10-15 minutes or until the carrots are completely tender and the liquid has slightly reduced in volume.

Leave the soup to cool a little, then blend to a purée in batches in a food processor or with a hand-blender. For a really smooth finish you can pass through a fine sieve into a bowl.

Reheat the soup gently and season lightly with pepper.

Ladle into bowls. Gently place a teaspoon of crème fraîche in the centre of each one, then scatter the chives over to serve.

typical nutritional content – *per portion*			
Energy Kcal (Calories)	102	Salt (g)	0.6
Fat (g)	4.0	Sugars (g)	14.0
of which saturates (g)	1.4		

garden pea and mint soup

This soup takes only minutes to prepare and is as good served cold as hot. It is really nice with a griddled slice of ciabatta, drizzled with a little extra-virgin olive oil.

Preparation time: 5 minutes • **Cooking time:** 10 minutes • *Serves 6*

what you need

2 tablespoons olive oil
1 onion, finely chopped
2 celery sticks, finely chopped
450g (1lb) frozen peas
6 fresh mint leaves, plus extra to garnish

900ml (1½ pints) chicken or vegetable stock
freshly ground black pepper

what you do

Heat the oil in a large pan. Add the onion and celery and sauté for about 5 minutes until softened but not browned, stirring occasionally. Add the peas, mint and stock and bring to the boil. Reduce the heat and simmer gently for 2-3 minutes, stirring, to allow the peas to cook through and the flavours to combine.

Pour the soup into a food processor and blend to a purée, or use a hand-held blender. Pour back into the pan. Season lightly with pepper and reheat gently.

Ladle the soup into warmed serving bowls set on plates. Garnish with mint and a good grinding of black pepper.

typical nutritional content – *per portion*			
Energy Kcal (Calories)	79	Salt (g)	0.5
Fat (g)	2.8	Sugars (g)	3.5
of which saturates (g)	0.4		

leek and potato soup with crème fraîche

This is a classic soup. Traditionally it is served chilled and is delicious with a squeeze of lemon juice and a dollop of natural yoghurt. It is equally good served hot with freshly baked brown soda bread.

Preparation time: 10 minutes • **Cooking time:** 30 minutes • *Serves 6*

what you need

2 tablespoons olive oil
450g (1lb) leeks, finely chopped
1 onion, finely chopped
225g (8oz) potatoes, diced
1 celery stick, diced
1 garlic clove, crushed
900ml (1½ pints) chicken or vegetable stock

150ml (¼ pint) low-fat milk
100g (4oz) half-fat crème fraîche
freshly ground white pepper
2 teaspoons fresh chives, snipped into little pieces

what you do

Heat the olive oil in a large heavy-based pan. Stir in the leeks, onion, potatoes and celery until well coated in olive oil. Add the garlic and season lightly with pepper, then place a parchment paper circle directly on top of the vegetables to keep in the steam. Cover the pan with a tight-fitting lid and allow the vegetables to cook on a low heat for about 10 minutes until they are soft and just beginning to brown.

Remove the lid and parchment paper from the pan and pour in the stock. Bring to the boil and simmer for about 5 minutes or until the potatoes are completely tender.

Purée the soup in batches in a food processor or use a hand-held blender. If you want a really smooth finish, pass through a fine sieve.

Pour into a clean pan and stir in the milk and most of the crème fraîche, putting aside some to garnish. Reheat gently to serve or, if you want it chilled, ladle it into a large bowl, cover with clingfilm and chill for at least 2 hours or overnight if possible. To serve, ladle into bowls, swirl in the rest of the crème fraîche and sprinkle the chives over.

typical nutritional content – *per portion*			
Energy Kcal (Calories)	129	Salt (g)	0.6
Fat (g)	7.3	Sugars (g)	1.5
of which saturates (g)	2.6		

mixed seafood chowder

Be careful not to overcook the fish for this recipe. As the fish has been cooked in the oven, the soup just needs to be warmed through before serving. You can also add a diced small parsnip or a couple of carrots to this soup for a change.

Preparation time: 15 minutes • **Cooking time:** 45 minutes • *Serves 6*

what you need

1 tablespoon olive oil
1 potato, peeled and diced
2 celery sticks, diced, plus some
leaves to garnish
25g (1oz) butter
25g (1oz) plain flour
600ml (1 pint) low-fat milk

1 onion, finely chopped
350g (12oz) firm white fish fillets,
skinned and any bones removed
150ml (¼ pint) fish stock
100g (4oz) large prawns, cooked and
peeled
freshly ground black pepper

what you do

Preheat the oven to 180°C/350°F/Gas Mark 4.

Heat the oil in a large pan. Add the potato and celery, stirring, then cover and cook gently until tender, stirring occasionally.

Meanwhile, make a white sauce. Melt the butter in a pan and remove from the heat. Stir in the flour, return to the heat and cook for 1-2 minutes, stirring. Gradually pour in the low-fat milk, whisking until smooth. Bring to the boil, then reduce the heat and simmer for 2-3 minutes, stirring continuously. Season lightly with pepper.

Spread the onion out in a small roasting tin and arrange the fish on top. Season lightly with pepper and pour about four tablespoons of the fish stock over. Cover loosely with tinfoil and bake for 10 minutes until just cooked through. Leave to cool a little, put the onion mixture to one side and then break up the fish into bite-sized pieces.

Add the white sauce, onion mixture and the remaining fish stock to the vegetables and gently bring to the boil, stirring well to combine. Blend with a hand-blender or in a food processor to a smooth purée and then fold in the cooked fish and prawns and simmer for 1-2 minutes to just heat through.

Ladle into bowls and garnish with celery leaves to serve.

typical nutritional content – *per portion*			
Energy Kcal (Calories)	191	Salt (g)	1.4
Fat (g)	7.5	Sugars (g)	6.5
of which saturates (g)	3.4		

roasted red pepper and tomato soup

Chargrilled peppers have the most wonderful, smoky sweetness. Collect as much of the juice as possible while you peel them, as it really has a great flavour. This soup tastes just as delicious when it is served well chilled on a warm summer's day.

Preparation time: 15 minutes • **Cooking time:** 1 hour • *Serves 6*

what you need

3 red peppers, halved, cored and seeded
2 tablespoons olive oil
1 teaspoon balsamic vinegar
½ teaspoon fresh thyme, chopped
1 large onion, finely chopped
2 garlic cloves, crushed

225g (8oz) plum tomatoes peeled, seeded and diced
2 tablespoons tomato purée
900ml (1½ pints) vegetable stock
1 tablespoon torn fresh basil, plus extra sprigs, to garnish
freshly ground black pepper

what you do

Preheat oven to 190°C/375°F/Gas Mark 5.

Arrange the pepper halves in a baking tin, cut-side up. Drizzle half of the olive oil over them and sprinkle the vinegar and thyme on top. Place in the oven and roast for 20-25 minutes until softened and charred.

When the peppers are cold enough to handle, remove the skins and discard, then chop the flesh roughly, keeping as much of the juice as possible. Set aside until needed.

Heat the remaining tablespoon of oil in a pan, add the onion and garlic and cook for 10 minutes until lightly golden, stirring occasionally. Add the pepper flesh with the plum tomatoes, tomato purée and stock and bring to the boil. Reduce the heat and simmer for 10-15 minutes until slightly reduced in volume. Add the basil and then blend with a hand-blender or food processor until smooth.

Season lightly with pepper and then ladle the soup into warmed bowls. Garnish with the basil sprigs to serve.

typical nutritional content – *per portion*			
Energy Kcal (Calories)	88	Salt (g)	0.5
Fat (g)	4.4	Sugars (g)	9.0
of which saturates (g)	0.6		

spicy parsnip and apple soup

Starchy root vegetables like parsnips are very good value in season and make deliciously filling soup. Enjoy as a light lunch or starter. If the consistency is a little too thick for your liking, add a little more low-fat milk or vegetable stock.

Preparation time: 15 minutes • **Cooking time:** 30 minutes • *Serves 6-8*

what you need

450g (1lb) parsnips
1 tablespoon olive oil
1 onion, finely chopped
225g (8oz) eating apples, peeled, cored and chopped
2 teaspoons medium curry powder

900ml (1½ pints) vegetable or chicken stock
300ml (½ pint) low-fat milk
freshly ground black pepper
½ teaspoon cumin seeds, to garnish (optional)

what you do

Peel the parsnips and cut into quarters, then cut into small pieces, removing any woody stems.

Heat the oil in a heavy-based pan, add the onion and cook for a few minutes until softened, stirring occasionally. Stir in the parsnips and apples, cover and cook for another few minutes, shaking the pan occasionally to prevent them from sticking.

Sprinkle the curry powder into the pan and cook, stirring for 1 minute. Pour in the stock with the milk and season with pepper. Bring to the boil, then reduce the heat to a gentle simmer and cook for 15 minutes until the parsnips are completely softened. Allow the soup to cool a little, then transfer to a food processor and blend until smooth, or use a hand-blender.

If using cumin seeds, place a small frying-pan over a medium heat and toast the seeds for a minute or two until they have darkened but aren't burned. Meanwhile, return the soup to the pan and reheat gently, stirring occasionally.

Serve the soup in warmed soup bowls, garnished with a sprinkling of cumin seeds (if liked).

typical nutritional content – *per portion*			
Energy Kcal (Calories)	86	Salt (g)	0.5
Fat (g)	2.9	Sugars (g)	8.6
of which saturates (g)	0.7		

wild mushroom soup

Mushroom soup made from wild mushrooms has the most extraordinarily intense flavour. Surprisingly enough, mushrooms that are a few days old and have darkened a bit make the best soup. Field mushrooms, which also have a great flavour, can be used instead of wild varieties.

Preparation time: 20 minutes • **Cooking time:** 20 minutes • *Serves 6-8*

what you need

15g (½oz) dried mushrooms
2 tablespoons olive oil
1 onion, finely chopped
2 garlic cloves, crushed
450g (1lb) wild or field mushrooms, sliced
600ml (1 pint) chicken or vegetable stock

50g (2oz) soft brown breadcrumbs
300ml (½ pint) low-fat milk
2 teaspoons half-fat crème fraîche
freshly ground black pepper
2 teaspoons fresh chives, snipped into little pieces

what you do

Soak the dried mushrooms in 150ml (¼ pint) of boiling water for 15 minutes. Drain and set aside the liquid. Finely chop the soaked mushrooms and set aside.

Heat the olive oil in a large pan and gently cook the onion for 3-4 minutes until softened but not browned. Add the garlic and cook for another 30 seconds or so, stirring. Increase the heat, add the fresh mushrooms and season lightly with pepper. Stir-fry for 3-4 minutes until the fresh mushrooms are just tender and have released their juices.

Pour the stock into the pan with the soaking liquid that you set aside, then add the soaked mushrooms with the breadcrumbs and milk. Bring to the boil, then reduce the heat and simmer for another 5 minutes or so until the mushrooms are completely tender, and the liquid has slightly reduced in volume and thickened.

Purée in batches in a food processor or with a hand-held blender. If necessary, pour back into the pan and then reheat gently.

Ladle into bowls and garnish with the crème fraîche and chives to serve.

typical nutritional content – *per portion*			
Energy Kcal (Calories)	86	Salt (g)	0.06
Fat (g)	4.2	Sugars (g)	3.4
of which saturates (g)	1.7		

tom yaam goong –
traditional spicy prawn soup

★ *RECIPE BY* Taweesak Trakoolwattana SABA *Clarendon St, Dublin 2*

You can experiment with Thai Tom Yaam Goong by adding your choice of fish and shellfish. Try it with a mixture of scallops, mussels, squid and crab claws for delicious results. Galangal root has a distinct peppery flavour and is used in curry pastes, stir-fried dishes and soups. You'll find it in larger supermarkets either fresh, dried or in a jar.

Preparation time: 15 minutes • **Cooking time:** 15 minutes • *Serves 4*

what you need

900ml (1½ pints) chicken stock
50g (2oz) lemongrass stalks, outer layers removed and thinly sliced
75g (3oz) piece galangal root, peeled and sliced (see introduction)
75g (3oz) small pink shallots, chopped
6 kaffir lime leaves (fresh or frozen)
8 red bird's eye chillies, sliced (wear rubber gloves)
2 dessertspoons chilli paste in oil

50ml (2fl oz) Thai fish sauce (nam pla)
50ml (2fl oz) freshly squeezed lime juice
2 teaspoons caster sugar
20 raw peeled tiger prawns, thawed if frozen
175g (6oz) oyster or button mushrooms, trimmed and sliced
15g (½oz) fresh coriander leaves, to garnish

what you do

Put the chicken stock into a large pan and heat until simmering. Add the lemongrass, galangal, shallots, kaffir lime leaves and bird's eye chillies. Bring back to a simmer and cook for a few minutes to allow all of the flavours to combine.

Add the chilli paste in oil to the chicken-stock mixture and then season with the fish sauce, lime juice and sugar. Add the prawns and mushrooms and cook for a minute or two until the prawns have turned pink and the mushrooms are tender.

Ladle into serving bowls and scatter the coriander leaves over to serve.

typical nutritional content – *per portion*			
Energy Kcal (Calories)	71	Salt (g)	2.5
Fat (g)	2.3	Sugars (g)	4.5
of which saturates (g)	0.1		

winter vegetable and lentil soup

This soup is definitely a meal in itself and certainly won't break the bank. You can leave out a vegetable if you don't have it to hand, or substitute one for another. A bouquet garni is a small bunch of herbs – usually a mixture of parsley stems, thyme and a bay leaf – tied together in muslin or with a piece of string and used to flavour stocks, soups and stews. You could substitute a teaspoon of chopped fresh thyme, if necessary.

Preparation time: 15 minutes • **Cooking time:** 45 minutes • *Serves 6*

what you need

2 tablespoons olive oil
1 large onion, finely chopped
2 small leeks, thinly sliced
2 carrots, chopped
2 celery sticks, chopped
2 garlic cloves, finely chopped
1.2 litres (2 pints) vegetable stock

4 large, ripe tomatoes, peeled and roughly chopped
100g (4oz) red lentils
1 bouquet garni (see introduction)
freshly ground black pepper
1 tablespoon fresh flat-leaf parsley, roughly chopped

what you do

Heat the oil in a large pan and add the onion and leeks. Cook gently for a few minutes until softened. Stir in the carrots, celery and garlic and cook for another 4-5 minutes, stirring occasionally, without allowing the vegetables to brown.

Pour the stock into the pan and add the tomatoes, lentils and bouquet garni. Season lightly with pepper, bring to the boil, then reduce the heat, cover and simmer gently for about 30 minutes or until the lentils are completely tender. Remove the bouquet garni.

Pour into bowls. Scatter the parsley over to serve.

typical nutritional content – *per portion*			
Energy Kcal (Calories)	138	Salt (g)	0.6
Fat (g)	4.7	Sugars (g)	8.5
of which saturates (g)	0.7		

healthy tips
fats explained

Fat is an essential nutrient. It protects joints and vital organs such as the kidneys, and is a source of energy. It also provides the fat-soluble vitamins A, D and E and essential fatty acids.

The total amount of fat and the type of fat that is eaten is important. For heart health and general health we need to limit all types of fat, but especially saturated fat.

Fats in food are a mixture of:

- Saturated fats.
- Unsaturated fats, which can be either monounsaturated fats or polyunsaturated fats.
- Trans fats.

Saturated fats
What effect do they have?
Saturated fats can raise your 'bad' or LDL cholesterol and increase your chances of getting heart disease or stroke.

Sources
You find saturated fats in foods like butter, hard margarine, lard, cream, cheese, fatty meat, cakes, biscuits and chocolates. Certain vegetable oils such as coconut oil and palm oil are also high in saturated fat. Check the food labels on processed and ready-made meals for the amount of saturated fats.

Monounsaturated fats
What effect do they have?
Monounsaturated fats can help lower the amount of 'bad' or LDL cholesterol in your blood and reduce your chances of heart disease or stroke.

Sources

Monounsaturated fats are found in many foods but the main sources include olive, peanut and rapeseed/canola oil and their spreads, as well as avocados, seeds and some nuts, e.g. cashew, almonds and peanuts.

Polyunsaturated fats

There are two main types of polyunsaturated fats: omega 3 fats and omega 6 fats. These fats are sometimes called essential fats because our bodies cannot make them and we have to get them from the food we eat.

Omega 3 fats

What effect do they have?

Omega 3 fats can help your heart maintain a healthy rhythm and prevent blood clots from forming. They can also help to lower another type of fat in the blood called triglycerides.

Sources

Omega 3 fats are found in oily fish such as salmon, mackerel, trout, herring and sardines. Tuna is also an oily fish. However, if you're opting for tinned tuna, make sure the label says that omega 3 fats have been replaced, as these healthy fats are normally lost during the tinning process.

Omega 6 fats

What effect do they have?

Omega 6 fats can help to lower 'bad' LDL cholesterol and reduce your chances of heart disease.

Sources

Omega 6 fats are found mainly in vegetable oils such as sunflower, safflower, corn, soya-bean and sesame oils. Soya beans and some nuts, e.g. walnuts, hazelnuts and brazil nuts, are also good sources.

Trans fats

What effect do they have on cholesterol levels?

Trans fats reduce the level of 'good' HDL cholesterol and increase the level of 'bad' LDL cholesterol in the blood.

Sources

Trans fats are mainly found in processed foods such as cakes, biscuits, pastries and deep-fried foods. If a food's list of ingredients contains the words 'hydrogenated oils' or 'hydrogenated fat', it is likely to contain trans fats.

Tips to reduce your fat intake

- Choose fewer cakes, pastries, biscuits and processed meats.
- All oils are almost 100% fat, including olive oil. A good non-stick pan helps to start foods off with very little or no fat at all. A non-stick low-fat spray, or an oil spray that allows the minimum amount of oil to be used, are available in most supermarkets.
- Choose lean meats. Trim fat off meat and skin off chicken.
- Drain oil from cooked dishes containing minced meat or casseroles.
- Regular cheese-eaters could try grated low-fat cheddar instead of full-fat cheese, especially in cooking, on toast or in toasted sandwiches.
- A strong dressing, such as wholegrain mustard or relish, offers a tasteful, zesty alternative to spread or butter.

Swap it!

swap	for	save
Full-fat mayonnaise	Low-fat mayonnaise	2.5 grams of fat for every teaspoon
Butter	Reduced fat spread	2 grams of fat for every teaspoon
Salad dressing	Low-fat/fat-free dressing	Up to 12 grams of fat on a salad
Full-fat milk	Low-fat milk	1 gram of fat in every cup of tea or coffee
Frying with oil	Use a non-stick frying pan (1 teaspoon)	About 4.6 grams of fat and spray oil (4 sprays)
Full-fat cheddar cheese (50g)	Low-fat cheddar cheese (50g)	9 grams of fat

For more information visit **www.irishheart.ie** or see the Irish Heart Foundation's leaflet on cholesterol for more information on the links between fat and cholesterol.

Main Course
Fish

tasty baked cod

★ RECIPE BY Caroline Morahan *Actress and Television Presenter*

We all know that fish is a great way to stay heart-healthy. It is also wonderful for your skin, nails and hair. The only problem for me is that I am not a big fish fan! However, this recipe is one that I make all the time, as it is just so delicious. If you don't want to use cod, try this recipe with hake or haddock. For the best results, always choose fish fillets from the centre of the cut and ask at the fish counter to ensure that all the skin and bones have been removed.

Preparation time: 15 minutes • Cooking time: 35 minutes • Serves 4

what you need

450g (1lb) potatoes, peeled or scrubbed clean, keeping the skins
3 tablespoons olive oil
4 ripe plum tomatoes, halved and cut into thick slices
1 red onion, cut into rings and separated

1 large yellow pepper, seeded and cut into chunks
2 tablespoons capers, drained
12 Kalamata olives, pitted
4 x 150g (5oz) cod fillets, skinned and boned
freshly ground black pepper

steamed asparagus to serve

what you do

Preheat the oven to 200°C/400°F/Gas Mark 6.

Cut the potatoes into 0.5cm (¼in) slices and arrange in a single layer in a roasting tin lined with non-stick parchment paper. Add one tablespoon of the olive oil and season lightly with pepper. Toss until evenly coated, then roast for 15-20 minutes or until cooked through and lightly golden.

Meanwhile, arrange the tomatoes in the bottom of an ovenproof dish and scatter the onion and yellow pepper over them. Sprinkle the capers on top with the olives and then drizzle a tablespoon of the olive oil over. Arrange the cod fillets on top and drizzle the remaining tablespoon of olive oil over. Roast in the oven for 8-10 minutes until cooked through and tender. The time will depend on the thickness of the fillet.

Arrange the potato slices on warmed plates and spoon the cod and vegetable mixture on top, drizzling over any cooking juices left in the dish. Serve at once with the steamed asparagus.

typical nutritional content – *per portion*			
Energy Kcal (Calories)	344	Salt (g)	1.7
Fat (g)	11.6	Sugars (g)	8.6
of which saturates (g)	1.9		

steamed hake with mustard and chive dressing

Hake is a tasty fish that is usually good value. Alternatively, you could use salmon, whiting, cod or haddock with excellent results. This mustard and chive dressing also tastes great with chicken.

Preparation time: 10 minutes • Cooking time: 10 minutes • *Serves 4*

what you need

For the fish parcels
4 x 175g (6oz) hake fillets, preferably from the centre cut, pin bones removed
1 teaspoon fresh chives, snipped into little pieces
a little olive oil

For the dressing
2 teaspoons wholegrain mustard

1½ teaspoons white-wine vinegar
2 tablespoons olive oil
1-2 teaspoons fresh chives, snipped into little pieces
freshly ground black pepper

steamed baby new potatoes and mangetout, to serve

what you do

Cut out four sheets of parchment paper and brush lightly with olive oil, then season lightly with pepper and scatter the chives over them. Place one piece of hake on each sheet. Fold in the sides of each parcel to enclose the hake. Twist the edges to seal. Place in a large steamer set over a pan of simmering water. Cover with a tight-fitting lid and steam for 5-6 minutes. The hake should look opaque (not transparent) when you unwrap it and it should flake slightly when pierced with the tip of a sharp knife, but it should still be moist.

Meanwhile, in a liquidiser, blend together the mustard and the vinegar. Pour the oil into the mustard mixture in a steady stream, whisking vigorously as you do so. Season with pepper.

Place the hake fillets on warmed plates. Add the chives to the dressing and spoon the dressing over the fillets. Serve with baby new potatoes and mangetout.

typical nutritional content – *per portion*			
Energy Kcal (Calories)	305	Salt (g)	0.6
Fat (g)	9.1	Sugars (g)	4.0
of which saturates (g)	1.3		

fish pie

★ *RECIPE BY* Maeve Higgins *Comedian*

Feel free to experiment with the combination of fish, depending on what is available. If you choose fish fillets that are all roughly the same thickness they will all poach in the same amount of time so it saves a lot of hassle!

Preparation time: 15 minutes • **Cooking time:** 1 hour • *Serves 4-6*

what you need

550g (1¼lb) potatoes, peeled, cut into chunks
1 small onion, roughly chopped
1 fresh thyme sprig
1 small bay leaf
a few black peppercorns
500ml (17fl oz) low-fat milk, plus extra for the mashed potato

3 eggs
750g (1¾lb) haddock, salmon, cod or whiting fillets or use a mixture
100g (4oz) mushrooms, sliced
1 tablespoon softened butter
2 tablespoons plain flour
1 tablespoon fresh parsley, chopped
freshly ground white pepper

what you do

Cook the potatoes in a pan of water for 15-20 minutes until tender.

Meanwhile, place the onion in a large pan with the thyme, bay leaf, peppercorns and milk. Bring to the boil and simmer for 3-4 minutes. Set aside to infuse for 10 minutes, then strain and put the strained milk to one side.

Drain and mash the potatoes until smooth and add enough milk to give a creamy but firm consistency.

Place the eggs in a pan with water and simmer for 10-12 minutes until hard-boiled, then shell and roughly chop.

Lower the fish fillets into the infused milk, then bring to a simmer and cook for 3 minutes or until the fish is just tender. Transfer to a plate, then roughly flake, discarding the skin and bones. Strain the milk – you'll need 350ml (12fl oz) for the sauce.

Place the mushrooms in a small pan of boiling water for 2 minutes. Drain and set aside until needed. Melt the butter in a pan, then add the flour and stir over a low heat for 1 minute. Gradually add the strained milk, beating until smooth. Simmer for 2-3 minutes until nicely thickened. Season lightly with pepper and stir in the parsley.

Preheat the oven to 180°C/350°F/Gas Mark 4.

Spread a layer of the flaked fish in the bottom of the ovenproof dish. Arrange a layer of hard-boiled eggs with a few spoons of the sauce on top of the fish. Top this with a layer of the mushrooms and some more sauce.

Spread the mashed potatoes on top and bake for 25-30 minutes until bubbling and golden.

Serve the fish pie straight to the table in its ovenproof dish.

typical nutritional content – *per portion*			
Energy Kcal (Calories)	328	Salt (g)	0.5
Fat (g)	11.6	Sugars (g)	5.4
of which saturates (g)	3.8		

grilled mackerel fillets with indian spiced potatoes and raita

★ *RECIPE BY* Sebastian Scheer PEPLOE'S *St Stephen's Green, Dublin 2*

This dish is perfect for a summer's evening. Of course the mackerel could be cooked on the barbecue but this oven method really helps to keep the fish moist. Just be careful not to overcook the fish, as it can dry out very quickly and become tasteless.

Preparation time: 10 minutes ● **Cooking time:** 25 minutes ● *Serves 4*

what you need

For the mackerel and spiced potatoes
8 medium-sized new potatoes
2 tablespoons olive oil
1 onion, minced
2 large garlic cloves, minced
1 teaspoon garam masala
2 tablespoons fresh coriander, chopped
8 x 75g (3oz) mackerel fillets, cleaned and any bones removed
juice of ½ lemon, pips removed

For the raita
¼ teaspoon cumin seeds
275g (10oz) natural yoghurt
1 cucumber, peeled, seeded and cut into small dice
3 spring onions, finely chopped
1 garlic clove, crushed
1 teaspoon fresh mint, chopped, plus extra sprigs to garnish
freshly ground black pepper

what you do

Place the potatoes in a pan of cold water and bring to the boil. Cover and cook for 15-20 minutes until tender. Drain and leave to cool completely, then cut into slices approximately 1cm (½in) thick.

Heat half of the olive oil in a large non-stick frying-pan and gently fry the onion and garlic for 6-8 minutes until golden brown, stirring occasionally. Stir in the garam masala and transfer to a bowl. Wipe out the frying-pan and return to the heat, add the remaining tablespoon of olive oil. Sauté the potatoes until crispy and golden brown. Sprinkle the onion mixture over and fold in the fresh coriander, then season with a little black pepper.

Meanwhile, preheat the grill to a medium heat. Arrange the mackerel fillets on a sturdy baking tray and season with black pepper. Add a few drops of lemon juice, then turn them over so they are skin-side up. Place under the grill for 5 minutes, then turn them over to brown the flesh, which will be nearly cooked by now and should need only a minute or two. Set aside for a few minutes to rest.

To make the raita, toast the cumin seeds by dry-frying them for a few minutes until they begin to pop in the pan, then set aside.

Place the yoghurt in a bowl and stir in the cucumber, spring onions, garlic, toasted cumin seeds and mint. Season with a little pepper and garnish with mint.

Arrange the potatoes in the centre of serving plates and place two mackerel fillets on each plate on top of the potatoes. Add a dollop of the raita to serve. The remainder of the raita can be served separately at the table.

typical nutritional content – *per portion*			
Energy Kcal (Calories)	498	Salt (g)	0.4
Fat (g)	30.1	Sugars (g)	8.9
of which saturates (g)	6.1		

spaghetti with a spicy tomato sauce

Even if you don't like anchovies, try this delicious sauce as you don't really get an anchovy taste, or if you prefer you could leave them out altogether.

Preparation time: 10 minutes • **Cooking time:** 20 minutes • *Serves 4*

what you need

450g (1lb) dried spaghetti
1 tablespoon olive oil
1 small onion, finely chopped
1 red chilli, seeded and finely chopped
(wear rubber gloves)
2 garlic cloves, finely chopped
400g (14oz) tin chopped tomatoes
50g (2oz) tin anchovy fillets, drained
and chopped

100g (4oz) pitted black olives,
drained
1 tablespoon small capers, drained
1 tablespoon fresh basil, chopped
1 tablespoon fresh flat-leaf parsley,
chopped
3 tablespoons freshly grated
Parmesan cheese

what you do

Cook the spaghetti in a large pan of boiling water for 10-12 minutes until tender but still with a little bite.

Meanwhile, heat the oil in a heavy-based saucepan and add the onion, chilli and garlic. Cook for 1-2 minutes until the onion is softened but not coloured.

Add the tomatoes to the onion mixture with the anchovies and cook for 2-3 minutes, stirring occasionally. Add the olives and capers and continue to cook for 10-15 minutes until well reduced in volume and thickened.

Drain the pasta, then return to the pan and add the spicy tomato sauce with the basil and parsley. Toss well together.

Divide between warmed pasta bowls or plates. Scatter the Parmesan over to serve.

typical nutritional content – *per portion*			
Energy Kcal (Calories)	506	Salt (g)	2.9
Fat (g)	11.4	Sugars (g)	7.4
of which saturates (g)	2.9		

steamed irish salmon with whipped pea and garlic purée and saffron roasted peppers

★ RECIPE BY Derry Clarke L'ECRIVAIN Lower Baggot Street, Dublin 2

Ask your fishmonger for a skinned and boneless piece of fillet. Fresh salmon should have no odour and look translucent with nice firm flakes. If buying pre-packed fish check that the flesh is soft and springs back when pressed.

Preparation time: 15 minutes • Cooking time: 40 minutes • Serves 4

what you need

For the saffron roasted peppers
2 red peppers
1 tablespoon olive oil
1 tablespoon sunflower oil
2 shallots, finely chopped
2.5cm (1in) fresh root ginger, peeled and minced
1 garlic clove, minced
1 teaspoon saffron strands, soaked in a little hot water
2 teaspoons fresh mixed herb (such as flat-leaf parsley, tarragon and chervil), chopped

For the salmon
150ml (¼ pint) dry white wine
1 carrot, chopped
1 onion, chopped
1 celery stick, chopped
1 fresh rosemary sprig
4 lemongrass stalks
4 x 150g (5oz) salmon fillets, skinned and boned

For the whipped pea and garlic purée
450g (1lb) frozen peas
knob of butter
2 garlic cloves, crushed
4 tablespoons low-fat milk
freshly ground black pepper

what you do

Preheat the grill to hot. Arrange the peppers on a grill rack and grill for 20-30 minutes until charred and blistered, turning regularly. Transfer to a large bowl and cover with clingfilm. Leave the peppers to cool completely, then peel, discarding the cores and seeds. Cut the flesh into slices.

Heat the olive oil and sunflower oil in a frying-pan. Add the shallots, ginger and garlic and cook for a couple of minutes until softened but not browned. Stir in the saffron mixture and cook for another minute or so, then season lightly with pepper. Transfer to a bowl and fold in the peppers and herbs. Cover with clingfilm and set aside at room temperature until needed.

To prepare the salmon, pour 600ml (1 pint) of water into the bottom half of a steamer and add the wine, carrot, onion, celery and rosemary. Bring to a simmer.

Meanwhile, peel off the tough outer stalk from each stick of lemongrass and then use one stick as a skewer for the each piece of salmon. Arrange above the simmering vegetables in the steamer and cook gently for 5-7 minutes or until the salmon is just cooked through and tender.

Meanwhile, make the whipped pea and garlic purée. Cook the peas in a pan of boiling water for 3-4 minutes until tender. Heat the butter in a separate pan and sauté the garlic for 20 seconds without browning. Drain the peas and add to the garlic mixture with the milk. Using a hand-blender, blend to a smooth purée. Season lightly with pepper.

Divide the whipped pea and garlic purée between warmed plates and arrange the salmon skewers on top. Spoon around the saffron roasted peppers to serve.

typical nutritional content – *per portion*			
Energy Kcal (Calories)	480	Salt (g)	0.3
Fat (g)	25.1	Sugars (g)	11.4
of which saturates (g)	5.0		

salmon with lime, ginger and coriander parcels

This has to be one of the best ways to cook salmon, but it is important not to overcook it. When the parcels are opened the salmon should still be pink inside. The flesh should give slightly, but not too much when gently pressed; if it is wobbly or jelly-like, then it is undercooked.

Preparation time: 10 minutes • Cooking time: 15 minutes • Serves 4

what you need

4 x 175g (6oz) salmon fillets, skinned and boned
2 teaspoons fresh root ginger, grated
finely grated rind and juice of 1 lime
2 garlic cloves, crushed
4 tablespoons fresh coriander, roughly chopped

freshly ground black pepper
lime wedges, to garnish

fresh tomato salad and steamed wild and basmati rice, to serve

what you do

Preheat the oven to 190°C/375°F/Gas Mark 5.

In a small bowl mix the ginger, lime rind and juice and garlic. Next, take four pieces of parchment paper about 27cm (11in) square and place a salmon fillet in the middle of each one. Season lightly with pepper and spoon the lime mixture over. Fold the long sides of the parchment paper inwards and then fold the remaining sides in, making small parcels.

Place the parcels on a baking sheet and bake for 8-10 minutes or until the salmon is just cooked through and tender; this will depend on the thickness of the fillets.

Open the salmon parcels and scatter the coriander over them, then garnish each one with a lime wedge.

Serve the salmon in their parcels on warmed plates, with tomato salad and rice if liked.

typical nutritional content – *per portion*			
Energy Kcal (Calories)	548	Salt (g)	0.2
Fat (g)	19.4	Sugars (g)	2.8
of which saturates (g)	3.3		

asian fishcakes with cucumber relish

These Asian-style fishcakes are really delicious and very easy to prepare. Choose any firm-fleshed white fish fillets such as hake, haddock, cod, ling or pollock, depending on what is freshest on the day. If you don't fancy using tiger prawns, white crab meat would also work well.

Preparation time: 15 minutes • Cooking time: 10 minutes • *Serves 4*

what you need

For the Asian fishcakes
2.5cm (1in) piece fresh root ginger, peeled and finely chopped
2 garlic cloves, finely chopped
15g (½oz) bunch fresh coriander, roots intact and chopped
2 spring onions, chopped
1 red chilli, seeded and finely chopped (wear rubber gloves)
1 tablespoon Thai fish sauce (nam pla)
350g (12oz) white fish fillets, skinned, boned and chopped

225g (8oz) raw peeled tiger prawns
2 tablespoons sunflower oil

For the cucumber relish
½ cucumber, halved, seeded and very finely diced
1 small red onion, very finely chopped
1 tablespoon sweet chilli sauce
1 tablespoon fresh lime juice
2 teaspoons Thai fish sauce (nam pla)

75g (3oz) fresh radishes, trimmed, to serve

what you do

To make the Asian fish cakes, place the ginger in a food processor with the garlic, coriander, spring onions, chilli and fish sauce. Blend to form a paste, then add the white fish fillets and prawns. Continue to blend but use the pulse button to keep a slightly coarse texture. Form into 12 even-sized balls and then flatten slightly into patties.

Heat the oil in a large heavy-based frying pan and add the fish cakes. Cook for 2-3 minutes each side until cooked through and golden brown. Drain well on kitchen paper.

Meanwhile, make the cucumber relish. Place the cucumber in a bowl with the red onion, sweet chilli sauce, lime juice and fish sauce and mix well to combine. To serve, slice the radishes and lay them over the base of each plate. Arrange the fish cakes on top and add small spoonfuls of the cucumber relish.

typical nutritional content – *per portion*			
Energy Kcal (Calories)	182	Salt (g)	1.3
Fat (g)	6.6	Sugars (g)	2.7
of which saturates (g)	0.8		

seared tuna with asian pesto and asparagus

This is a recipe where only the best-quality tuna will do. Ask your fishmonger for sashimi-quality tuna, which basically means that it is good enough to eat raw. Tuna cooks really quickly because it has such an open texture that the heat penetrates easily, so be careful not to overcook it.

Preparation time: 10 mins + 1 hr chilling • Cooking time: 15 mins • *Serves 4*

what you need

450g (1lb) sashimi-quality tuna
3 tablespoons poppy seeds
20 asparagus spears
lime wedges and fresh coriander
sprigs, to garnish

For the Asian pesto
50g (2oz) raw shelled unsalted peanuts
1 small roasted pepper, from a jar,
drained

1 garlic clove, crushed
1 teaspoon root ginger, freshly grated
1 Thai red hot chilli, seeded and
roughly chopped (wear rubber gloves)
finely grated rind and juice of 1 lime
15g (½oz) mixture fresh flat-leaf
parsley, basil and mint
1 tablespoon Thai fish sauce (nam pla)
3 tablespoons rapeseed oil
1 tablespoon sesame oil

what you do

To make the pesto place the peanuts into a large frying-pan and toast for 3-4 minutes until just beginning to brown, then using a clean tea towel rub off their skins. Place in a liquidiser with the pepper, garlic, ginger, chilli, lime rind and juice, herbs and fish sauce. Pulse to form a coarse mix. Allow the motor to run and then add the rapeseed oil and sesame oil until they are well mixed.

Cut the tuna into 4 even-sized strips. Place the poppy seeds on a flat plate and then roll each tuna strip in the seeds and place on a piece of clingfilm. Wrap really tightly to form a long rounded sausage shape. Twist the clingfilm at each end. Do this to each piece and chill for at least 1 hour and up to 8 hours until ready to use.

When almost ready to serve, steam the asparagus for 4-6 minutes or until just tender; this will depend on the thickness of the spears.

Heat a large heavy-based frying-pan until very hot, unwrap the tuna and fry without oil making sure that you keep moving the tuna so it just cooks lightly. This will take 1-2 minutes. Allow to rest until the asparagus is ready.

Drain the asparagus and toss in one tablespoon of the Asian pesto. Place 5 asparagus spears on each plate in a line. Slice the tuna carefully and place along the line of the asparagus. Finish with a drizzle of the Asian pesto (the remainder can be served in a separate dish at the table) and garnish with the lime wedges and coriander sprigs.

typical nutritional content – *per portion*			
Energy Kcal (Calories)	300	Salt (g)	0.6
Fat (g)	18.9	Sugars (g)	3.0
of which saturates (g)	3.3		

spiced hake with coconut and spinach curry

Fish is very lean and tastes delicious in this curry. Coconut cream is the thick cream that rises to the top of a tin of coconut milk. Using low-fat coconut milk for this recipe won't compromise the taste.

Preparation time: 10 mins + 10 mins marinating • Cooking time: 15 mins • Serves 4

what you need

For the hake
2 teaspoons tandoori curry paste
2 teaspoons coconut cream (see introduction)
4 x 150g (5oz) hake fillets, boned and scaled
1 tablespoon sunflower oil

For the coconut and spinach curry
1 tablespoon sunflower oil
4 garlic cloves, finely chopped
12 fresh or dried curry leaves (optional)

2 teaspoons black mustard seeds
400g (14oz) tin low-fat coconut milk
2 red chillies, seeded and finely chopped (wear rubber gloves)
juice of 1 lime
1 tablespoon Thai fish sauce (nam pla)
350g (12oz) washed spinach, tough stalks removed
lime wedges, to garnish

rice, to serve

what you do

To prepare the hake, mix the tandoori curry paste in a small bowl with the coconut cream. Rub onto the fleshy side of the hake fillets. Set aside for about 10 minutes to allow the flavours to penetrate the flesh.

Meanwhile, make the coconut and spinach curry. Heat the oil in a wok, add the garlic and cook for a few seconds before adding the curry leaves (if using) and the mustard seeds.

When the mustard seeds start to pop, add the coconut milk and chillies, allow to simmer and reduce in volume for 3-4 minutes. Next stir in the lime, fish sauce and spinach. Cook for a couple of minutes until the spinach has just wilted, stirring occasionally.

Preheat the grill. Heat the oil in a large heavy-based frying-pan, then place the fish skin-side down. Cook for 3 minutes until the skin is really crispy. Then place under the grill for a minute or two until the flesh side is just cooked through.

Divide the curry into warmed wide-rimmed bowls and top each with a piece of spiced hake. Serve with rice, and garnish with lime wedges.

typical nutritional content – *per portion*			
Energy Kcal (Calories)	243	Salt (g)	1.5
Fat (g)	10.2	Sugars (g)	7.1
of which saturates (g)	2.6		

tagliatelle with creamy smoked haddock

It's the crème fraîche that gives this dish a deceptively creamy flavour – yet keeps the fat content low. Try to buy undyed smoked haddock if possible, and don't overcook it; this dish is so much nicer if the flakes of fish are moist and fresh. Overcooked smoked fish has a slightly harsh aftertaste.

Preparation time: 10 minutes • **Cooking time:** 25 minutes • *Serves 4*

what you need

450g (1lb) smoked haddock or smoked cod fillets (undyed if possible)
250g (9oz) packet dried egg tagliatelle
1 tablespoon olive oil
1 large shallot, finely chopped
1 garlic clove, crushed
250ml (8½fl oz) carton half-fat crème fraîche

1 teaspoon Dijon mustard
finely grated rind of ½ lemon
2 tablespoons fresh flat-leaf parsley, chopped
2 tablespoons freshly grated Parmesan cheese
freshly ground black pepper
lemon wedges, to garnish

green salad, to serve

what you do

Bring a large pan of water to the boil. Meanwhile, poach the haddock or cod in a sauté pan or deep frying-pan with enough cold water to keep the fillets covered. Bring to a simmer and cook for 3-4 minutes or until just cooked through; this will depend on the thickness of the fillets. Drain and, when cool enough to handle, remove the skin and break into large pieces, discarding any bones.

Add the tagliatelle to the boiling water and cook for 3 minutes or according to packet instructions until just cooked through and tender. Heat the oil in a frying-pan and sauté the shallot for 2-3 minutes until softened. Stir in the garlic and cook for another minute or so. Reduce the heat right down and very gently stir in the crème fraîche, mustard and lemon rind until just warmed through. Season generously with the pepper and stir in the parsley.

Drain the tagliatelle and return to the pan, then fold in the crème fraîche sauce with the smoked haddock. Divide between warmed wide-rimmed bowls and scatter the Parmesan over. Garnish with lemon wedges and serve with a separate bowl of salad.

typical nutritional content – *per portion*			
Energy Kcal (Calories)	489	Salt (g)	2.8
Fat (g)	17.0	Sugars (g)	6.6
of which saturates (g)	8.5		

healthy tips
time to cut down on salt

Salt in very small amounts is essential to your health. However, many people eat more than twice the amount of salt their bodies need. If you eat too much salt, this can increase blood-pressure levels and in turn increase your risk of a heart attack or stroke.

About 80% of the salt we eat comes from processed foods, fast food, canteen and restaurant food. About 10-15% is added at home in cooking or at the table and only 5% occurs naturally in food.

Eating less salt

- Gradually reduce the amount of salt you add at the table and during cooking.

- If you do need to use ready-meals, look for reduced-salt options.

- Get out of the habit of having instant high-salt foods like salted nuts or crisps at home. In fact, do not even put them in your shopping basket!

- Sea salt and rock salt have the same salt or sodium content as common salt and so can increase blood pressure. Salts described as low salt are mixtures of sodium and potassium, where potassium has been added to reduce the sodium content. If you have kidney failure, heart failure or have diabetes do not use a low-salt variety without medical advice.

Food labels can be confusing at the best of times, but even more so when it comes to salt. This is because it is usually the amount of sodium, rather than salt, that is listed on the label. To work out how much salt is in a food, you need to multiply the sodium figure by 2.5. For example, if a food has one gram of sodium per 100g – that means it has 2.5 grams of salt.

Swap it!

swap	for
Salt	Black pepper, herbs, spices, garlic and lemon juice
Stock cubes, gravy granules and ready-made sauces	Home-made stock or sauces
Processed meat	Lean fresh meat
Ready-meals	Home-cooked meals

For more information visit **www.irishheart.ie** or see the Irish Heart Foundation leaflet 'Time to Cut Down on Salt'.

healthy tips
fabulous fibre

Bread, cereals, potatoes, pasta and rice are starchy foods that are high in carbohydrate. They are the best source of energy for the body, provide many minerals and vitamins, and are naturally low in fat. They are high in fibre, naturally filling, and keep the bowels working properly. Research indicates that when increased amounts of these foods are eaten, it is easier to eat a lower fat diet.

There are two types of fibre: soluble fibre and insoluble fibre.

Soluble fibre is a soft fibre that can help to lower high levels of 'bad' LDL cholesterol. Oat bran and oat-based cereals, together with peas, beans and lentils, barley and fruits such as apples, strawberries and citrus fruits, are the best sources of soluble fibre.

Insoluble fibre helps to prevent and control bowel problems and is important in preventing certain cancers. The best sources are wheat bran, wheat or bran-based cereals, wholegrain foods like wholemeal bread, fruit and vegetables including skins and seeds.

How to eat more fibre

- Leave the skins on potatoes where possible.
- Add beans, peas and lentils to dishes.
- Add more vegetables and salads to your meals.
- Remember to drink plenty of water to help the fibre to work.

Swap it!

swap	for
Low-fibre breakfast cereal	High-fibre breakfast cereal
White bread	Wholegrain or wholemeal bread
Regular pasta and rice	Wholegrain pasta and rice

For more information visit **www.irishheart.ie** or read the Irish Heart Foundation's 'Good Eating' leaflet.

♥

Main Course
Pork

sizzling pork fajitas with tomato and avocado salsa

This is a great dish that all the family will enjoy. The pork can be marinated well in advance, leaving very little to do at the last minute. You can replace the pork with beef or chicken with equally good results.

Preparation time: 10 mins + 2 hrs marinating • Cooking time: 20 mins • *Serves 4*

what you need

For the fajitas
2 garlic cloves, crushed
finely grated rind and juice of 1 lime
1 teaspoon ground cumin
½ teaspoon ground coriander
good pinch paprika
3 tablespoons olive oil
450g (1lb) pork fillet, trimmed and
sliced into strips
1 large onion, thinly sliced
1 red and 1 yellow pepper, seeded and
cut into thin strips

8 soft flour tortillas
4 tablespoons half-fat crème fraîche

For the tomato and avocado salsa
1 large ripe tomato, diced
1 ripe avocado, peeled, diced and
stone removed
2 spring onions, finely chopped
1 mild red chilli, seeded and finely
chopped (wear rubber gloves)
freshly ground black pepper
fresh coriander leaves, to garnish

what you do

Place the garlic in a non-metallic dish with the lime rind and juice, cumin, coriander and paprika. Stir in half the olive oil. Fold in the pork strips and then cover with clingfilm and marinate in the fridge for up to 2 hours or overnight if possible.

To make the fajitas, heat the remaining olive oil in a large frying-pan and gently fry the onion and peppers for 6-8 minutes over a low heat until softened, stirring occasionally. Transfer with a slotted spoon to a bowl and keep warm.

Meanwhile, to make the salsa, place the tomato in a bowl with the avocado, spring onions and chilli. Mix well to combine. Season lightly with pepper and set aside at room temperature to allow the flavours to combine.

Reheat the frying-pan. Add the marinated pork strips and sauté for 4-6 minutes until cooked through and lightly golden. Return the onion and pepper mixture to the pan and stir-fry for another 2-3 minutes until well combined and heated through. Season lightly with pepper to taste.

Heat a frying or griddle pan. Add a soft flour tortilla and heat for 30 seconds until soft and pliable, turning once. Repeat with the remaining tortillas and stack them up on a warmed plate.

Transfer the sizzling pork mixture into a warmed bowl or on to a platter and garnish with the fresh coriander to serve. Pass around the warmed tortillas, salsa and crème fraîche, also garnished with the coriander leaves, allowing each person to assemble the fajitas themselves.

typical nutritional content – *per portion*			
Energy Kcal (Calories)	643	Salt (g)	2.1
Fat (g)	30.5	Sugars (g)	12.8
of which saturates (g)	9.6		

fillet of pork with calvados sauce

★ *RECIPE BY* Bobbie Smith LORUM OLD RECTORY *Bagenalstown, Co Carlow*

This pork fillet is flattened down into escalopes that are cooked until they're beautifully golden but still tender and moist. Calvados is a French apple brandy that is well worth having in the cupboard for cooking.

Preparation time: 10 minutes • Cooking time: 10 minutes • *Serves 4*

what you need

400g (14oz) pork fillet
2 eating apples
200ml (7fl oz) dry cider
(or unsweetened apple juice)
100ml (3½fl oz) chicken stock
25g (1oz) sugar

2 tablespoons white wine vinegar
25ml (1fl oz) Calvados (apple brandy)
2 tablespoons olive oil
freshly ground black pepper

steamed mangetout, to serve

what you do

Trim all visible fat from the pork and cut into four even-sized slices, about 2.5cm (1in) thick. Place one at a time between two sheets of clingfilm and beat with a rolling pin until very thin and about 15cm (6in) in diameter.

Peel, core and slice the apples. Put the peelings and cores to one side. Put the apples with two tablespoons of the cider into a pan. Cook slowly until you have a thick apple purée, stirring occasionally with a wooden spoon, then leave to cool.

In a separate pan, boil the peelings and cores of the apples with the cider or apple juice and stock until the liquid reduces in volume by half, then strain.

For the sauce, melt the sugar in a heavy-based pan over a gentle heat until it caramelises. When it starts to brown, add the cider-stock and one tablespoon of the vinegar. Boil for a few minutes. Add the Calvados, stirring continuously. Cook for several minutes, then taste, adding more vinegar and pepper if necessary.

Place a spoonful of apple purée on each pork escalope and fold over. Heat the olive oil in a large heavy-based frying-pan, add the escalopes and cook gently for about 3 minutes on each side until cooked through and nicely browned.

Lift onto warm plates. Spoon the sauce over, and serve with the steamed mangetout.

typical nutritional content – *per portion*			
Energy Kcal (Calories)	291	Salt (g)	0.9
Fat (g)	9.4	Sugars (g)	21.2
of which saturates (g)	2.0		

baked spicy spare ribs

Ask your butcher for nice meaty racks of pork spare ribs and make sure he trims off any visible fat. Of course, the ribs can also be barbecued but it's always best to cook them for the first hour in the oven and then just finish cooking them on the grill. This will help prevent the sticky glaze from burning.

Preparation time: 15 minutes • Cooking time: 1 hour 40 minutes • *Serves 6*

what you need

2 racks lean meaty pork spare ribs
(about 1.75kg or 4lb in total)

For the sauce
1 tablespoon sunflower oil
4 large garlic cloves, finely chopped
2 red chillies, seeded and finely
chopped (wear rubber gloves), or
2 tablespoons hot chilli sauce (use
both if you like things very hot!)

400g (14oz) tin whole peeled tomatoes
5 tablespoons cider vinegar
5 tablespoons clear honey
2 tablespoons Dijon mustard
good dash of Worcestershire sauce
300ml (½ pint) chicken stock
freshly ground black pepper

baked jacket potatoes and salad, to serve

what you do

Preheat the oven to 190°C/375°F/Gas Mark 5.

To make the sauce, heat the oil in a pan over a moderate heat. Add the garlic and fresh chillies (if using) and stir for about 30 seconds. Add the tomatoes, vinegar, honey, mustard, Worcestershire sauce, chilli sauce (if using), stock and season lightly with pepper. Bring to the boil over a high heat and mash down the tomatoes with a potato-masher or fork, then simmer for 15-20 minutes until well reduced in volume and thickened, stirring occasionally. Leave to cool a little and then, using a hand-blender, blend briefly, leaving a little texture in the sauce.

Cut each rack of ribs into two even-sized pieces and arrange on a wire tray in a large roasting tin. Brush with some of the sauce. Roast for 30 minutes. The excess fat will drain off into the roasting tin. Brush the ribs with more sauce and roast for another hour, turning and brushing with more sauce occasionally until the ribs are meltingly tender. Leave the ribs to rest for about 5 minutes.

Cut into individual ribs and arrange on warmed plates with jacket potatoes and plenty of salad to serve.

typical nutritional content – *per portion*			
Energy Kcal (Calories)	623	Salt (g)	1.6
Fat (g)	21.9	Sugars (g)	20.9
of which saturates (g)	7.6		

apple-glazed pork chops with dijon mash

These pork chops are cooked until they're beautifully golden but still tender and moist. The addition of the apple sauce gives them the most fantastic dark golden colour and sweet stickiness.

Preparation time: 15 minutes • Cooking time: 25 minutes • *Serves 4*

what you need

For the pork chops
4 x 125g (4½oz) boneless loin pork chops
1 tablespoon olive oil
12 fresh sage leaves
4 tablespoons Bramley apple sauce
(from a jar)
½ lemon, pips removed

For the Dijon mash
900g (2lb) floury potatoes such as
Roosters, cut into even-sized chunks
4-6 tablespoons low-fat milk
1 tablespoon Dijon mustard
freshly ground black pepper

sautéed spinach, to serve

what you do

Place the potatoes in a large pan of water. Bring to the boil, cover and simmer for 15-20 minutes or until the potatoes are tender without breaking up. Drain and return to the pan over a low heat to dry out.

Using a very sharp knife, carefully trim off any visible fat from the pork chops, rub all over with some of the olive oil and season lightly with pepper. Rub the rest of the olive oil on the sage leaves. Heat a heavy-based frying-pan over a high heat. Add the pork chops and give them about 3 minutes on each side, turning every minute. When they are nicely golden add the sage leaves to the pan and leave the chops for a further 30 seconds or so on each side to crisp up. Remove the sage to a plate and set aside. Spoon a tablespoon of the apple sauce over each chop and cook for another minute or so, turning so that they get nicely coated. Squeeze the lemon juice over and set aside for a few minutes to rest.

Mash the potatoes. Using a wooden spoon, beat in enough of the milk to make the mash smooth. Beat in the Dijon mustard and season lightly with pepper.

Divide the Dijon mash between warmed plates and arrange a pork chop to the side, spooning any pan juices over. Use the sage leaves to garnish. Add a mound of sautéed spinach to each plate to serve.

typical nutritional content – *per portion*			
Energy Kcal (Calories)	393	Salt (g)	0.8
Fat (g)	9.5	Sugars (g)	6.2
of which saturates (g)	0.8		

spicy chorizo pasta

The small amount of chorizo added to this chilli and peppers mixture gives this dish a really spicy flavour. To make this dish suitable for vegetarians leave out the chorizo and fold in a tin of haricot beans or chickpeas that have been rinsed and drained.

Preparation time: 10 minutes • Cooking time: 20 minutes • *Serves 4*

what you need

1 tablespoon olive oil
1 large onion, thinly sliced
2 red peppers, seeded and cut into strips
1 red chilli, seeded and finely chopped (wear rubber gloves)
2 garlic cloves, crushed
75g (3oz) raw chorizo, skinned and diced

2 x 400g (14oz) tins chopped tomatoes
2 tablespoons chopped fresh flat-leaf parsley or basil
350g (12oz) penne pasta
2 tablespoons freshly grated Parmesan cheese
freshly ground black pepper

salad, to serve

what you do

Heat the oil in a pan and gently cook the onion, peppers and chilli for 10 minutes until softened but not browned, stirring occasionally. Stir in the garlic and chorizo and cook for another few minutes until the chorizo starts to release its oil. Pour in the tomatoes and simmer for another 2-3 minutes until slightly reduced in volume and thickened, stirring occasionally. Stir in the parsley or basil and season lightly with pepper.

Meanwhile, cook the penne pasta for 10-12 minutes or according to instructions on the packet until cooked through and just tender. Drain well and mix with the tomato and chorizo sauce.

Divide between warmed wide-rimmed bowls and lightly scatter the Parmesan over the top. Serve with a bowl of salad straight to the table.

typical nutritional content – *per portion*			
Energy Kcal (Calories)	503	Salt (g)	0.6
Fat (g)	10.7	Sugars (g)	20.9
of which saturates (g)	3.4		

stir-fried pork with aromatic ginger greens

This is a great way to prepare green vegetables. The stir-frying ensures they keep their crunch while the hot sauce gives them a rich, almost nutty flavour. Choose one or a selection of the wide range of greens now readily available, such as sugar snap peas, French beans, mangetout, spinach, Swiss chard, Chinese pak choy, choy sum – or even finely shredded cabbage works well.

Preparation time: 10 mins + 15 mins marinating · **Cooking time:** 20 mins · *Serves 4*

what you need

450g (1lb) boneless loin pork chops
2 tablespoons dry sherry or rice wine
2 tablespoons soy sauce
1 teaspoon sesame oil
2 teaspoons cornflour
120ml (4fl oz) chicken stock
2 tablespoons sunflower oil

5cm (2in) piece fresh root ginger, peeled and finely grated
275g (10oz) mixed prepared greens (see introduction)
2 spring onions, finely shredded
1 long red chilli, cut into thin rings (wear rubber gloves) – optional

steamed brown rice, to serve

what you do

Trim any visible fat from the side of each pork chop. Thinly slice the pork. Place half of the sherry or rice wine and soy sauce in a shallow non-metallic dish and add the sesame oil and cornflour. Stir in the pork and set aside for 15 minutes (up to 24 hours covered with clingfilm in the fridge is fine).

Heat a wok until very hot. Place the remaining tablespoon of sherry and soy sauce in a small pan with the chicken stock, then bring to a simmer. Add half the sunflower oil and swirl it up the sides of the wok. Tip in the pork and stir-fry for 3-4 minutes until well cooked and lightly golden. Transfer to a plate.

Add the rest of the sunflower oil to the wok. Add the ginger and stir-fry for about 10 seconds. Tip in the greens and continue to stir-fry for 2-3 minutes until heated through and any leaves are just beginning to wilt, splashing a little water over occasionally to help the greens cook.

Return the pork to the wok, then stir in the hot stock mixture. Cook for another minute or so until bubbling, stirring regularly. Spoon the steamed rice into warmed large Oriental-style bowls and spoon the ginger pork and greens on top. Scatter the spring onions and the chilli (if using) over the stir-fry to serve.

typical nutritional content – *per portion*			
Energy Kcal (Calories)	511	Salt (g)	2.3
Fat (g)	15.2	Sugars (g)	3.7
of which saturates (g)	3.2		

roast loin of pork with pine nuts and apricot stuffing

★ *RECIPE BY* James Kehoe THE LORD BAGENAL INN *Co Carlow*

This has to be one of the tastiest cuts of pork and you'll find that a little goes a long way, making it an excellent choice for a Sunday lunch. Roast potatoes are really delicious cooked this way around the joint, basting in all the delicious juices.

Preparation time: 15 mins + soaking overnight ▪ Cooking time: 2 hrs ▪ *Serves 10-12*

what you need

1.75kg (4lb) loin of pork
1.5kg (3lb) even-sized medium
potatoes, peeled

For the stuffing
900g (2lb) ready-to-eat dried apricots
300ml (½ pint) cider (or unsweetened
apple juice)

1 tablespoon olive oil
3 tablespoons pine nuts
2 tablespoons fresh brown
breadcrumbs
2 egg yolks
freshly ground black pepper

steamed sugar snap peas, to serve

what you do

To make the stuffing, place the dried apricots in a glass (or other non-metallic) bowl with the cider or apple juice and set aside overnight to plump up. The next day, drain the apricots.

Heat the olive oil in a frying-pan and sauté the pine nuts until lightly golden. Add the apricots with the breadcrumbs and plenty of freshly ground black pepper. Remove from the heat and leave to cool a little, then stir in the egg yolks to bind the stuffing.

Preheat the oven to 190°C/375°F/Gas Mark 5.

Place the loin of pork, fat side down, on the work surface. Cut between the fat and meat of the loin and remove the layer of fat with the rind. Cut the loose white fat from the rind and discard, putting the rind to one side. Turn the loin over. Spread the stuffing on top of the loin and place the rind back on top. Tie with fine string at 2.5cm (1in) intervals.

Place the loin in a roasting tin and put in the oven. Sprinkle with a little pepper once while the joint is cooking. Roast for 30 minutes.

Meanwhile, bring the potatoes to the boil in a large pan of water and cook for 4 minutes, then drain and return to the pan. Shake vigorously to fluff up the potatoes.

Remove the roasting tin from the oven and place the potatoes around the joint, basting them with the cooking juices, then return to the oven and roast for another hour or until the pork is cooked and completely tender.

Transfer the pork to a warmed serving plate and leave it to rest, uncovered, for about 20 minutes. Meanwhile, give the roast potatoes a good shake in the tin and roast for another 20 minutes until crisp and golden brown.

Cut the string from the rested pork joint. Cut off the crackling and discard.

Carve the pork into thin slices and arrange on warmed plates with the roast potatoes and sugar snap peas to serve.

typical nutritional content – *per portion*			
Energy Kcal (Calories)	476	Salt (g)	0.2
Fat (g)	10.9	Sugars (g)	30.9
of which saturates (g)	0.6		

pasta carbonara

A true Italian carbonara does not actually have any cream in it, yet the sauce coats the pasta and tastes delicious. Try it – you will be pleasantly surprised! If you don't fancy the bacon, try strips of smoked salmon instead, which works well.

Preparation time: 5 minutes • Cooking time: 12 minutes • *Serves 6*

what you need

500g (1lb 2oz) packet dried spaghetti
1 tablespoon olive oil
3 garlic cloves, peeled and halved
225g (8oz) rindless lean smoked back rashers, cut into strips
3 large eggs

100g (4oz) freshly grated Parmesan cheese
freshly ground black pepper

salad, to serve

what you do

Cook the spaghetti for 8-10 minutes or according to the instructions on the packet until just cooked through and tender.

Meanwhile, heat a large frying-pan. Add the olive oil and the garlic and gently sauté for 3-4 minutes until the garlic is golden but not turning brown. Remove the garlic and discard.

Add the rashers to the garlic-flavoured oil and sauté for 3-4 minutes until they are cooked through and have started to become crisp. Remove from the heat.

Meanwhile, beat the eggs in a bowl with most of the Parmesan, keeping a little Parmesan to garnish, then season with plenty of freshly ground black pepper. When the pasta is almost ready, turn the heat on low under the bacon to just warm through. Take out a mugful of the pasta cooking water and set aside.

Drain the pasta and return it to the still hot pan. Add the egg and cheese mixture along with a splash of the pasta water from the mug. Toss well to combine, adding a little more pasta water if necessary – you should need somewhere between 50-120ml (2-4fl oz). The heat of the water and the pasta cooks the egg lightly. Do not reheat or the eggs will scramble.

Fold the bacon and the garlic-flavoured oil into the pasta mixture.

Divide between warmed wide-rimmed bowls. Give each one a good grinding of black pepper and scatter the rest of the Parmesan over the top. Serve immediately with a large bowl of salad.

typical nutritional content – *per portion*			
Energy Kcal (Calories)	449	Salt (g)	1.6
Fat (g)	13.8	Sugars (g)	3.1
of which saturates (g)	5.4		

tangy pork with mango salsa

This is a great dish when you've got people to feed but want to enjoy the company. It can be made up to a day in advance and the added bonus is that the flavour just continues to improve. It also works brilliantly on the barbecue on medium-hot coals.

Preparation time: 35 mins • Cooking time: 25 mins + 10 mins resting • *Serves 4*

what you need

500g (1lb 2oz) pork fillet, well trimmed

For the marinade
1 tablespoon hot chilli sauce
1 tablespoon sunflower oil
1 tablespoon dry sherry
1 tablespoon light soy sauce

For the salsa
1 red pepper, seeded and diced
1 ripe mango, peeled and diced (stone discarded)
3 spring onions, finely chopped
1 tablespoon hot chilli sauce

steamed baby new potatoes and French beans, to serve

what you do

To prepare the marinade, mix together the hot chilli sauce, sunflower oil, sherry and soy sauce in a small bowl and then spread all over the pork fillet in a shallow non-metallic dish. Cover with clingfilm and set aside for at least 30 minutes, but overnight in the fridge is best.

To make the salsa, place the pepper in a bowl with the mango, spring onions and hot chilli sauce. Cover with clingfilm and set aside at room temperature for 20 minutes to allow the flavours to combine or, if keeping it any longer, chill until needed.

Preheat the grill to medium. Arrange the pork fillet on a grill rack and cook for 10-12 minutes on each side or until cooked through and tender; this will depend on the thickness of the fillet.

Remove to a warm platter and leave to rest for at least 10 minutes, then carve into thin slices. Arrange on warmed plates with the salsa. Add some baby new potatoes and French beans to serve.

typical nutritional content – *per portion*			
Energy Kcal (Calories)	392	Salt (g)	1.4
Fat (g)	7.7	Sugars (g)	13.2
of which saturates (g)	2.0		

crispy parma ham and quinoa salad

Quinoa is readily available from health food shops. It is easy to prepare and its fluffy texture and slightly nutty flavour make it an excellent alternative to white rice or couscous. When cooked, its grains quadruple in size and become almost translucent. Removing the skins of the cooked broad beans is a labour of love but well worth the effort, not just for taste but for the colour as well. If using frozen broad beans the skins will come off really easily once they are defrosted.

Preparation time: 10 minutes • Cooking time: 30 minutes • *Serves 4-6*

what you need

200g (7oz) quinoa (see introduction)
juice of 1 lemon
4 tablespoons extra-virgin olive oil
300g (10oz) broad beans or peas, podded (see introduction)
250g (9oz) petit pois, thawed if frozen

100g (4oz) mangetout, trimmed
handful fresh mint leaves
1 garlic clove, roughly chopped (or 6 wild garlic leaves)
4 slices Parma ham
freshly ground black pepper

what you do

Cook the quinoa according to the packet instructions. Drain well in a sieve, then tip into a bowl and add the lemon juice and one tablespoon of the olive oil. Mix well to combine and then leave to allow the flavours to infuse.

Meanwhile, place the broad beans or peas in a pan of boiling water for 2-3 minutes or until tender. Drain and refresh under cold running water, then tip into a bowl. Then, if using broad beans, slip out of their skins. In a separate pan of boiling water, place the petits pois and mangetout for 2 minutes, then drain and quickly rinse with cold water.

Place the mint in a blender with the two tablespoons of olive oil, the garlic (or wild garlic leaves) and a little pepper as seasoning. Blend to a smooth paste and then use to dress the broad beans (or peas), petit pois and mangetout, and set aside until needed.

Heat a heavy-based frying-pan until very hot and add a thin film of olive oil. Cook the slices of Parma ham for a minute or so until crisp and lightly golden, turning once – you will probably have to do this in batches. Drain well on kitchen paper.

Divide the quinoa salad between plates, then roughly break up the Parma ham and scatter on top to serve.

typical nutritional content – *per portion*			
Energy Kcal (Calories)	257	Salt (g)	0.6
Fat (g)	11.3	Sugars (g)	4.4
of which saturates (g)	1.8		

healthy tips

heart-healthy eating on a budget

By making a few small changes to your shopping habits, healthy eating need not be expensive. The key is to plan carefully, shop wisely and try to avoid waste.

Try the following tips:

- Use the Food Pyramid (*see page 230*) to plan your list, checking roughly the number of servings you need.
- It's best to not shop while hungry.
- Bring only enough money for the foods on your list.
- Add beans, peas and lentils to stews, curries, sauces, soups and salads. This will make meat go further and increase the fibre in the meal.
- Compare food labels – find out what you're paying for.
- Buy fruit and vegetables in season. Or try buying frozen which is just as nutritious.
- Look out for special offers but remember to check 'best before' dates.
- Tinned tomatoes are great as they can be used in stews, soups and sauces, as a pizza topping or to 'stretch' ready-made sauces.

Swap it!

swap	for
Shopping without a list	Making a shopping list and sticking to it
Deciding each day what to buy for that day's meals	Planning weekly meals so that you know generally what amounts of food you need to put on your list
Buying processed ready-meals	Making your own 'ready-meals' is cheaper than buying a prepared product and you have more control over the fat and salt content – make a large amount and freeze for busy times
Buying large quantities of food	Buying only as much food as you think you will use – shop where you can buy the exact amounts you need
Buying the same food brand every time	Shopping around and comparing prices – more expensive brands are usually displayed at eye-level in shops so check top and bottom shelves for cheaper options

Main Course
Poultry

chicken curry

★ *RECIPE BY* Brenda Costigan *Food Writer*

Hot and juicy, with aromatic steam wafting up from the plate, this kind of food is great on colder days. This chicken curry certainly fits the bill. All manner of cuts, from more expensive chicken breasts to good-value chicken thighs, can be used. Equally, a whole chicken can be bought and cut up into portions.

Preparation time: 15 minutes • Cooking time: 45 minutes • *Serves 4*

what you need

4 x 150g (5oz) chicken breasts on the bone, skinned
2 garlic cloves, finely chopped
1 onion, chopped
1 carrot, chopped
1 celery stick, chopped

For the curry sauce
1 tablespoon vegetable oil
1 onion, finely chopped
2 garlic cloves, chopped
2-4 teaspoons mild curry powder

25g (1oz) plain flour
2 teaspoons tomato purée
1 teaspoon fresh root ginger, grated
2 teaspoons mango chutney
½ cooking apple, peeled, cored and diced
1 banana, peeled and sliced
50g (2oz) raisins
fresh coriander sprigs to garnish

steamed brown rice, to serve

what you do

Place the chicken breasts in a deep-sided pan with 600ml (1 pint) of water, the garlic, onion, carrot and celery. Bring to a gentle simmer and cook for about 15 minutes until just cooked through and tender. The amount of time will depend on the type of chicken you use. Remove the chicken to a plate and then skim off any excess fat from the cooking liquid (stock) before putting it to one side – you'll need 450ml (¾ pint) in total.

To make the curry sauce, wipe out the pan and use to heat the oil. Add the onion and cook for a few minutes until softened but not browned. Stir in the garlic and cook for another 20 seconds, then stir in the curry powder (the amount you use depends on how spicy you like your curry) and cook for a minute or two. Next add in the flour and stir over the heat for another minute or so. Remove from the heat and gradually add in the stock. Using a whisk, stir briskly until you have achieved a slightly chunky sauce.

Whisk the tomato purée into the curry sauce with the ginger and mango chutney and then add the apple and bring to the boil, stirring. Reduce the heat, cover with a lid and cook gently for about 5 minutes until slightly reduced in volume and thickened. Return the chicken to the pan with the banana and raisins. Bring to a gentle simmer and cook for 8-10 minutes or until the chicken is piping hot and all the flavours have nicely blended together.

Arrange on warmed plates with the brown rice and then garnish with the coriander sprigs to serve.

typical nutritional content – *per portion*			
Energy Kcal (Calories)	540	Salt (g)	0.5
Fat (g)	6.9	Sugars (g)	22.2
of which saturates (g)	1.3		

chicken skewers with dried fruit couscous

★ *RECIPE BY* Tim Daly The Strawberry Tree *The Brooklodge Hotel and Wells Spa, Co Wicklow*

Feel free to substitute chicken thighs for the chicken breasts. The thighs have a great flavour and tend to be much more succulent – they also work very well cooked on the barbecue.

Preparation time: 15 mins + 1 hr marinating • Cooking time: 15 mins • *Serves 4*

what you need

For the chicken
4 x 100g (4oz) skinless chicken breast fillets
1 tablespoon olive oil
2 garlic cloves, crushed
½ teaspoon each ground cumin, turmeric and paprika
juice of 1 lemon

For the couscous
1 tablespoon olive oil
1 small onion, finely chopped
1 garlic clove, crushed
¼ teaspoon each ground cumin, cinnamon and ginger

50g (2oz) dates, stoned and chopped
50g (2oz) dried ready-to-eat apricots, chopped
50g (2oz) toasted flaked almonds
225g (8oz) couscous
juice of ½ lemon
2 tablespoons chopped fresh coriander, plus extra sprigs to garnish
225 ml (8fl oz) vegetable stock
freshly ground black pepper
4 lemon wedges, to garnish

what you do

To prepare the chicken, cut each chicken breast fillet in half lengthways and place in a shallow non-metallic dish with the olive oil, garlic, cumin, turmeric, paprika and lemon juice. Mix well to combine. Cover with clingfilm and leave to marinate for about 2 hours in the fridge (up to 24 hours is fine). Thread the chicken pieces onto eight 15cm (6in) wooden skewers that have been soaked in water for at least 30 minutes to prevent them from burning.

To prepare the couscous, heat the olive oil in a non-stick frying-pan. Add the onion and garlic and sauté for 3-4 minutes until softened. Stir in the cumin, cinnamon and ginger and cook for another minute or so. Mix well and season with pepper. Stir in the dates, apricots and almonds and take off the heat.

Place the couscous in a large bowl. Heat the vegetable stock in a saucepan until boiling and then pour over the couscous. Cover tightly with clingfilm and leave to stand for 5 minutes before gently separating the grains with a fork. Fold in the lemon juice and coriander with the dried fruit and onion mixture and season with pepper. Set aside at room temperature to allow the flavours to develop.

Heat a large cast-iron griddle pan (or a large frying-pan) until very hot. Add the marinated chicken skewers and cook for 8-10 minutes until cooked through and lightly charred, turning occasionally.

Remove from the heat and leave to rest for a couple of minutes before arranging on plates with the couscous. Garnish with the coriander sprigs and lemon wedges to serve.

typical nutritional content – *per portion*			
Energy Kcal (Calories)	598	Salt (g)	0.9
Fat (g)	15.7	Sugars (g)	10.1
of which saturates (g)	1.7		

orange chicken stir-fry

★ *RECIPE BY* Catherine Fulvio Ballyknocken House & Cookery School *Co Wicklow*

This is an excellent stir-fry that could be on the table in less than 30 minutes, making it a perfect mid-week meal that all of the family will enjoy. Of course you could replace the chicken with pork fillet for great results. Pak choy is a green vegetable that is now grown in Ireland, but spinach would also work well.

Preparation time: 10 minutes • Cooking time: 20 minutes • *Serves 4*

what you need

finely grated rind and juice of
2 oranges
½ teaspoon Thai fish sauce
(nam pla) – optional
1 teaspoon light brown sugar
1½ tablespoons light soy sauce
2 garlic cloves, finely chopped
1 tablespoon vegetable oil
2 x 100g (4oz) skinless chicken fillets,
diced

1 red chilli, finely sliced into rings
(wear rubber gloves)
2 spring onions, finely sliced
2 pak choy, roughly chopped
small handful fresh coriander leaves,
roughly chopped
2 handfuls bean sprouts

brown rice, to serve

what you do

Combine the orange rind and juice, fish sauce (if using), brown sugar, soy sauce and garlic in a small bowl. Set aside until needed.

   Heat a wok until very hot, then add the oil and swirl up the sides. Tip in the chicken and chilli and stir-fry for 2-3 minutes or until the chicken is just tender and lightly golden.

   Add the spring onions to the chicken mixture and stir-fry for another minute or so. Pour in the orange mixture and continue to stir-fry for another 2-3 minutes.

   Add the pak choy to the chicken and orange mixture, with the coriander and bean sprouts, and cook for another minute, tossing the wok occasionally until everything is nicely combined. Divide the orange chicken stir-fry into Oriental-style bowls and serve with the brown rice.

typical nutritional content – *per portion*			
Energy Kcal (Calories)	245	Salt (g)	1.0
Fat (g)	4.6	Sugars (g)	5.1
of which saturates (g)	0.8		

quick chicken tikka wraps with greek-style yoghurt

These wraps would also be delicious with a dollop of cucumber raita that takes only minutes to prepare. Mix grated cucumber into the yoghurt with a little chopped fresh mint, finely grated garlic and a pinch of ground cumin. Season lightly with pepper and mix well to combine.

Preparation time: 10 mins + 15 mins marinating • Cooking time: 10 mins • Serves 4

what you need

6 tablespoons Greek-style yoghurt
2 teaspoons tandoori curry paste or powder
2 teaspoons garam masala (from a jar)
2 garlic cloves, grated
2 teaspoons fresh root ginger, grated
400g (14oz) skinless chicken fillets,
cut into thin strips
2 tablespoons sunflower oil

1 onion, thinly sliced
4 large soft flour tortilla wraps
1 Little Gem lettuce, trimmed
and shredded
2 tablespoons mango chutney
freshly ground black pepper
handful fresh coriander sprigs,
to garnish

what you do

Mix 4 tablespoons of the yoghurt with the curry paste or powder, garam masala, garlic and ginger in a bowl. Add the chicken and mix really well. Season lightly with pepper and, if you have the time, allow to marinate covered with clingfilm for at least 15 minutes or overnight in the fridge.

Heat the sunflower oil in a wok or a large frying-pan. Add the onion and stir-fry for a few minutes until it is beginning to caramelise and turn golden. Add the chicken and cook rapidly over a high heat for about 2-3 minutes or until the chicken is just cooked through and tender.

Meanwhile, heat a heavy-based frying-pan and add a soft flour tortilla wrap. Cook for 10 seconds or so on each side until heated through and lightly puffed up. Repeat with the remainder of the wraps.

To serve, scatter first the shredded lettuce and then the spiced chicken mixture over the tortilla wraps, then spoon the remaining yoghurt and the mango chutney on top and wrap up to enclose the filling. Cut each wrap in half and arrange on plates. Garnish with coriander sprigs, if liked.

typical nutritional content – *per portion*			
Energy Kcal (Calories)	399	Salt (g)	1.1
Fat (g)	10.0	Sugars (g)	11.7
of which saturates (g)	2.5		

roast chicken with mushroom and courgette stuffing

★ RECIPE BY Kevin Dundon Dunbrody Country House Hotel Co Wexford

This roast chicken is filled with a delicious mushroom and courgette stuffing before being roasted. I like to serve it with a red onion gravy that is packed full of flavour, and plenty of steamed broccoli completes the meal.

Preparation time: 20 mins · Cooking time: 1 hr 50 mins · *Serves 4*

what you need

For the chicken
1.5-1.8kg (3-4lb) oven-ready
free-range chicken
2 tablespoons olive oil
1 small onion, diced
1 medium courgette, diced
50g (2oz) wild mushrooms, trimmed
and finely chopped
finely grated rind of 1 lemon
1 teaspoon fresh sage, chopped
100g (4oz) fresh brown breadcrumbs

1 egg, beaten
3 streaky bacon rashers

For the red onion gravy
300ml (½ pint) chicken stock
1 tablespoon softened butter
1 small red onion, diced
1 tablespoon plain flour
2 tablespoons red wine
freshly ground black pepper

steamed long stemmed broccoli, to serve

what you do

Preheat oven to 200°C/400°F/Gas Mark 6.

Heat the oil in a medium saucepan and add the onion, courgette and wild mushrooms. Cook over a very low heat for 5-6 minutes until all ingredients are softened completely. Mix in the lemon rind, sage and breadcrumbs. Season this mixture lightly with pepper and then add enough beaten egg to bind the stuffing. Leave to cool. Stuff the cavity of the chicken with cooled stuffing and secure the flap with a cocktail stick. Weigh the bird and calculate the cooking time, allowing 20 minutes per 450g (1lb) plus 20 minutes. Place the chicken in a roasting tin and season lightly with pepper. Lay the bacon over the breast to prevent it from going dry. Roast for 15-20 minutes, then reduce the oven temperature to 180°C/350°F/Gas Mark 4 and cook until the chicken is cooked through and tender. Test the thickest part of the thigh with a fine skewer; when cooked, the juices will run clear. Remove from the oven and leave to rest in a warm place for 20 minutes loosely covered with tinfoil.

Meanwhile, make the red onion gravy. Heat the stock in a saucepan until boiling. Melt the butter in a separate small saucepan. Add the red onion and sauté for about 5 minutes until softened but not browned. Sprinkle the plain flour over and stir until the onion is evenly coated. There is no need to take the pot off the direct heat to do this because browning of the flour will further develop the flavour of the sauce.

Pour the red wine into the sautéed onions and allow to simmer down, and then gradually add the stock, whisking continuously. Simmer for a few minutes until slightly reduced in volume and thickened. Drain off any excess fat from the roasting tin and whisk any remaining juices into the gravy – these will add a tremendous flavour and body to the gravy. Season with pepper to taste.

Carve the chicken and arrange on serving plates with the stuffing and long-stemmed broccoli. Pour some of the red onion gravy around to serve.

typical nutritional content – *per portion*			
Energy Kcal (Calories)	465	Salt (g)	1.9
Fat (g)	23.7	Sugars (g)	4.4
of which saturates (g)	7.1		

sesame coated chicken with red cabbage salad

★ *RECIPE BY* John Healy *Television Presenter*

I'm quite partial to Asian food and this dish combines my favourite Asian textures and flavours. The Asian-inspired dressing for the red cabbage salad uses light miso paste, which is optional but is well worth seeking out. You'll find it in the Oriental section of some of the larger supermarkets or any Asian market. A little goes a long way but it does keep well in the fridge once opened.

Preparation time: 15 mins • Cooking time: 12 mins + 5 mins resting • *Serves 4*

what you need

For the dressing
2 teaspoons prepared English mustard
1 teaspoon light miso paste (optional)
2 teaspoons rice vinegar
1 teaspoon light soy sauce
2 tablespoons rapeseed oil
1 teaspoon sesame oil

For the red cabbage salad
1 small red onion, finely sliced
175g (6oz) red cabbage, finely sliced
(core removed)
50g (2oz) baby spinach leaves

For the chicken
4 x 75g (3oz) skinless chicken breast
fillets
4 teaspoons light olive oil
2 tablespoons mixed sesame seeds
lime wedges and 2 finely sliced spring
onions, to garnish

what you do

To make the dressing, put the mustard and miso (if using) in a bowl with the vinegar and soy sauce. Mix well to combine, then slowly drizzle in the rapeseed and sesame oil until smooth, whisking continuously.

Put the red onion, cabbage and spinach into a bowl and pour the dressing over them, then toss until everything is lightly coated. Set aside at room temperature to allow the flavours to combine.

Heat a heavy-based frying-pan to very hot. Brush the chicken breasts with two teaspoons of the light olive oil and then roll in the sesame seeds.

Add the remaining two teaspoons of light olive oil to the heated frying-pan and add the coated chicken fillets. Cook for 4-5 minutes on each side or until cooked through and tender. Transfer to a warm plate and cover loosely with tinfoil for 5 minutes to rest.

Carve the rested sesame coated chicken into slices on the diagonal. Divide the salad between plates and arrange the sliced chicken on top. Sprinkle the spring onions over and garnish with lime wedges to serve.

typical nutritional content – *per portion*			
Energy Kcal (Calories)	227	Salt (g)	0.7
Fat (g)	14.2	Sugars (g)	3.3
of which saturates (g)	1.7		

roast chicken breasts with spiced red chilli butter

This is a great dish packed full of flavour that can be made in advance and just popped into the oven when you're ready to eat. Remember, it is best to wear rubber gloves when preparing chillies to avoid skin irritation. For a milder flavour, replace the chilli with two crushed garlic cloves.

Preparation time: 10 minutes • Cooking time: 50 minutes • *Serves 4*

what you need

40g (1½oz) butter, softened
2 tablespoons fresh coriander, chopped, plus extra to garnish
1 mild red chilli, seeded and finely chopped (wear rubber gloves)
4 x 175g (6oz) part-boned chicken breasts (skin on)

juice of ½ lemon
4 cherry tomato vines, each with 5-7 tomatoes
1 teaspoon olive oil
freshly ground black pepper

what you do

Preheat the oven to 200°C/400°F/Gas Mark 6.

Place the butter in a bowl and beat in the coriander and chilli.

Make three slashes on each chicken breast to a depth of about 5mm (¼in), then arrange in a roasting tin, skin-side up. Spread with the spiced butter, pushing it down into the slashes. Squeeze the lemon juice on top.

Place the chicken in the oven and roast for 25 minutes, then remove from the oven and arrange the tomatoes around the edges of the tin. Lightly drizzle them with the olive oil and season lightly with pepper. Roast for another 20 minutes until the chicken breasts are completely tender and the skin is crisp and golden. The tomatoes should also be tender and the skins should have split.

Arrange on warmed plates and garnish with coriander to serve.

typical nutritional content – *per portion*			
Energy Kcal (Calories)	280	Salt (g)	0.3
Fat (g)	15.6	Sugars (g)	3.2
of which saturates (g)	5.4		

chicken chompers with sweet chilli dip

Kids just love chicken nuggets and these taste so much nicer than any of the shop-bought ones. For a change, try using turkey escalopes that you cut into strips. They also freeze very well and are handy to have in the freezer for busier times.

Preparation time: 10 minutes • Cooking time: 50 minutes • *Serves 6*

what you need

100g (4oz) sliced brown bread
50g (2oz) freshly grated Parmesan cheese
2 eggs
2 tablespoons low-fat milk
25g (1oz) plain flour

450g (1lb) boneless skinless chicken breasts
2 tablespoons olive oil
100g (4oz) half-fat crème fraîche
1 tablespoon sweet chilli sauce
freshly ground black pepper

what you do

Cut the crust off the slices of bread and spread out on a baking sheet overnight in a warm place; or bake them in a preheated oven at 100°C/200°F/Gas Mark ¼ for 25-30 minutes until crisp but not browned. Place in a food processor and blend to fine breadcrumbs (they will keep well in an airtight container for up to two weeks).

Place the breadcrumbs and Parmesan in a shallow dish, season with pepper and mix well. Break the eggs into a separate shallow dish, add the milk and lightly whisk to combine. Put the flour on a flat plate. Cut the chicken breast fillets into bite-sized chunks, then dust in the flour, tip into the beaten egg and finally roll in the breadcrumb mixture, making sure at each stage that each piece of chicken is well coated. Arrange on a baking sheet lined with parchment paper and chill for 10 minutes to allow the coating to firm up (or up to 24 hours in the fridge is fine).

Preheat the oven to 180°C/350°F/Gas Mark 4.

Drizzle the olive oil evenly over the chicken nuggets and bake for 12-15 minutes until crisp and golden brown, turning once to ensure they cook evenly.

To make the sweet chilli dip, place the crème fraîche in a small bowl and stir in the sweet chilli sauce. Drain the chicken chompers on kitchen paper.

Arrange on warmed plates with separate bowls of the sweet chilli dip to serve.

typical nutritional content – *per portion*			
Energy Kcal (Calories)	252	Salt (g)	0.7
Fat (g)	11.7	Sugars (g)	1.9
of which saturates (g)	4.6		

turkey and leek stroganoff

For those evenings when you want instant comfort food, you can't go far wrong with this variation on an old favourite. Chicken or beef could be substituted for the turkey, depending on what takes your fancy.

Preparation time: 10 minutes • Cooking time: 45 minutes • *Serves 4*

what you need

225g (8oz) wild and basmati rice
1 tablespoon sunflower oil
knob of butter
2 small leeks, trimmed, sliced on the diagonal
175g (6oz) chestnut mushrooms, sliced
1 garlic clove, crushed
450g (1lb) turkey breast steaks, cut into strips

¼ teaspoon paprika, plus a little extra to garnish
1 tablespoon white wine vinegar
4 tablespoons white wine
150ml (¼ pint) chicken stock
1 teaspoon Dijon mustard
2 teaspoons tomato purée
4 tablespoons sour cream
freshly ground black pepper

what you do

Bring a large pan of water to the boil. Add the rice and return to the boil, then give it a good stir and turn down to a low heat. Cook according to the packet instructions.

Heat a pan over a medium heat. Add the oil and butter and then add the leeks. Sauté for 2-3 minutes until softened but not browned.

Increase the heat and add the mushrooms to the pan with the garlic. Season lightly with pepper and continue to sauté for another 2-3 minutes until tender. Scatter in the turkey and then sprinkle in the paprika and cook for another minute or two, stirring.

Add the white wine vinegar and allow to simmer right down, then add the wine with the stock, mustard and tomato purée and simmer for a few minutes until reduced in volume by half, stirring occasionally.

Stir the sour cream into the pan, bring to a simmer, then reduce the heat and simmer gently for a couple of minutes until the sauce has thickened and slightly reduced in volume and the turkey is tender but still moist.

Divide the rice between warmed plates and spoon the turkey and leek stroganoff alongside. Finish with a light dusting of paprika to serve.

typical nutritional content – *per portion*			
Energy Kcal (Calories)	438	Salt (g)	1.1
Fat (g)	10.9	Sugars (g)	2.3
of which saturates (g)	4.6		

healthy tips
portion size matters

It's about quantity as well as quality. As well as looking at the types of food we eat we also need to look at the portion size, especially when aiming to be a healthy weight. Follow the Food Pyramid recommendations *(see page 230)*.

Be aware that you may be eating more than you realise. For example, are you grazing – picking away at food while watching the telly or in the car? If you are grazing, you may not realise how much you are eating.

Even making one change to your eating habits can make a real difference.

Swap it!

swap	for
A large plate or bowl	A smaller plate or bowl – and you don't have to clear your plate
Eating quickly	Eating slowly and enjoying every mouthful – it takes 20 minutes for your stomach to realise it's full
Extra meats and fats	Fruit and vegetables
Danish pastry (673 calories; 32g fat) three times a week	A scone (174 calories; 7g fat) – over a year you could save 1½ stone

For more information visit **www.irishheart.ie** or see the Irish Heart Foundation's 'Good Eating' leaflet.

Main Course
Beef

homemade beef burgers with guacamole

Homemade beef burgers taste delicious. The guacamole also makes a wonderful dip that can be served with vegetable crudités or wholemeal pitta-bread fingers.

Preparation time: 15 minutes • **Cooking time:** 15 minutes • *Serves 6*

what you need

For the burgers
500g (1lb 2oz) round steak, trimmed and coarsely chopped
2 tablespoons onion, finely grated
1 tablespoon Dijon mustard
handful of fresh coriander leaves, plus extra to garnish
1 teaspoon olive oil

For the guacamole
1 ripe avocado
1 small garlic clove, crushed
1 tablespoon fresh lime juice
1 tomato, peeled, seeded and chopped
a few drops Tabasco sauce

To serve
6 small soft round multi-seed brown rolls
1 Little Gem lettuce, broken into leaves
3 ripe tomatoes, sliced
1 small red onion, finely sliced
freshly ground black pepper

what you do

Place the steak, onion, mustard and coriander in a food processor. Blend until combined but be careful not to over-process. Shape the mixture into six burgers. Place on a plate, then cover with clingfilm and place in the fridge until needed (this helps to firm them up).

Preheat a griddle or frying-pan for about 4 minutes on a high heat. Turn the heat down to medium. Brush the olive oil on the heated pan and add the burgers. Use a spatula to lightly press down on them, making sure each burger is in full contact with the pan. Cook them to your liking for 3-4 minutes on each side – you may need to cook them in two batches.

To make the guacamole, cut the avocado in half lengthways and scoop out the flesh, discarding the stone. Mash the flesh with a fork. Mix in the garlic, lime juice, tomato, Tabasco and season lightly with pepper.

When the burgers are cooked, transfer to another plate and wipe the griddle or frying-pan clean with kitchen paper. Halve the brown rolls and lightly toast.

Arrange the bottom halves of the rolls on warmed plates and top with the lettuce, tomato slices and red onion. Cover each one with a burger and add a good dollop of the guacamole. Scatter the coriander over and place the brown roll tops over the guacamole to serve.

typical nutritional content – *per portion*			
Energy Kcal (Calories)	220	Salt (g)	0.6
Fat (g)	12.4	Sugars (g)	3.2
of which saturates (g)	4.4		

beef stew with a crispy potato crust

What could be nicer than a plate of steaming beef stew on a cold winter's day? The potato topping in this recipe is slightly more tricky to make than regular mash, but it is worth it. Crispy on the outside, soft inside, your guests will be begging for the recipe. Use Golden Wonder, Cyprus or another starchy potato for the best results.

Preparation time: 15 minutes • Cooking time: 1 hour 50 minutes • *Serves 6-8*

what you need

2 tablespoons olive oil
800g (1lb 12oz) chuck beef steak
3 onions, thinly sliced
1 teaspoon fresh thyme, chopped
2 tablespoons plain flour
500ml (16.9fl oz) can stout
300ml (½ pint) beef stock

1 teaspoon light brown sugar
1 tablespoon red wine vinegar
900g (2lb) potatoes, as even-sized as possible (see introduction)
15g (½oz) butter
freshly ground black pepper

what you do

Preheat the oven to 160°C/325°F/Gas Mark 3.

Trim the beef well and cut into 5cm (2in) cubes. Using a large saucepan, heat half the oil and tip in the beef. Quickly brown on all sides, then transfer to a plate with a slotted spoon. Set aside.

Add the onions to the saucepan and cook for about 5 minutes until lightly golden, stirring occasionally. Add the thyme and cook for 1 minute, stirring. Sprinkle in the flour and continue to cook over a low heat for another minute or so, stirring constantly.

Gradually pour in the stout, stirring until smooth after each addition. Pour in the stock, stirring to combine and season lightly with pepper, then add the sugar and vinegar. Bring to the boil, then remove from the heat and tip in the beef, mixing well to combine.

Transfer the stew to an ovenproof dish. Cover with a lid. Put into the oven and cook for 1 hour until the beef is almost tender and the liquid has reduced in volume and slightly thickened.

Meanwhile, place the potatoes in a large pan of water. Bring to the boil, then reduce the heat and simmer for 10 minutes until they are just starting to soften but are not cooked through. Drain, then quickly cool under cold running water before coarsely grating.

Sprinkle the grated potato over the beef stew and drizzle with the remaining tablespoon of oil, then dot with the butter. Return to the oven for 30 minutes until the potato crust is nice and crispy.

Serve straight to the table.

typical nutritional content – *per portion*			
Energy Kcal (Calories)	313	Salt (g)	0.4
Fat (g)	9.9	Sugars (g)	5.4
of which saturates (g)	3.4		

lasagne

★ *RECIPE BY* Georgina Campbell *Food Writer and Editor,* GEORGINA CAMPBELL'S IRELAND GUIDE

This is a variation on classic lasagne, which uses low-fat ingredients and cooking methods to provide a healthier alternative without losing any of the flavour. For an even healthier alternative be less generous with the Parmesan or use low-fat cheese.

Preparation time: 30 minutes • Cooking time: 2 hours • *Serves 6*

what you need

For the meat sauce
450g (1lb) lean minced beef
1 large onion, finely chopped
2 large cloves garlic, finely chopped
1 celery stick, finely chopped
1 large carrot, finely chopped

375ml (13fl oz) beef or chicken stock
2 x 400g (14oz) tins chopped tomatoes
1 teaspoon dried oregano
1 bay leaf
1 tablespoon tomato purée

For the white sauce
600ml (1 pint) low-fat milk,
plus 3 tablespoons
1 small onion, peeled and studded
with 3 whole cloves
1 bay leaf
2 tablespoons cornflour
1 teaspoon mustard

12 dried lasagne sheets
3 tablespoons freshly grated
Parmesan cheese
freshly ground black pepper

salad, to serve

what you do

Heat a large saucepan over a moderate heat, add the minced beef and break it down with a wooden spoon. Keep moving the mince around until the meat is lightly browned. Drain off all excess fat, then add the onion, garlic, celery and carrot and cook gently for about 10 minutes until the vegetables are softening, stirring occasionally. Add the stock and bring to the boil. Cook for another couple of minutes, stirring. Add the tomatoes, oregano, bay leaf, tomato purée and 120ml (4fl oz) of water. Season lightly with pepper and stir well, then simmer very gently for about an hour until a thick sauce is produced, stirring occasionally and adding a little water if the mixture seems to be drying out.

To make the white sauce, rinse a pan with cold water and then add the 600ml (1 pint) of low-fat milk, the clove-studded onion and the bay leaf. To allow the flavours to penetrate the milk, slowly bring to the boil then remove from the heat and leave for 15 minutes. Strain.

Blend together the cornflour and the remaining three tablespoons of low-fat milk, then gradually add the strained milk. Return to the pan and cook over a moderate heat, stirring all the time to make a smooth sauce. Add mustard and season lightly with black pepper.

Preheat the oven to 180°C/350°F/Gas Mark 4.

To assemble the lasagne, spread a thin layer of the meat sauce in the bottom of an ovenproof dish that is about 28 x 20cm (11½ x 8ins). Arrange a single layer of pasta sheets over the sauce. Top this with another layer of the meat sauce, then a layer of white sauce and a light sprinkling of Parmesan. Repeat layers as before, finishing with a layer of pasta and keeping some of the white sauce to top the pasta. Sprinkle lightly with Parmesan and bake for about 45 minutes until bubbling and golden brown.

Bring straight to the table in its dish and serve with salad.

typical nutritional content – *per portion*			
Energy Kcal (Calories)	420	Salt (g)	1.1
Fat (g)	11.8	Sugars (g)	15.7
of which saturates (g)	5.4		

harissa glazed beef with roasted sweet potato wedges

This recipe uses a sirloin of beef, which is a very popular roasting joint with very little waste. However, you could use other cuts that are suitable for roasting or even a butterflied leg of lamb would work well. Look out for jars of harissa paste in the supermarket. It is a Moroccan chilli paste that, once opened, keeps well in the fridge for up to one month.

Preparation time: 10 mins + 2 hrs marinating

Cooking time: 1 hr 30 mins + 10 mins resting • *Serves 12*

what you need

1 large garlic bulb
1.5kg (3lb) sirloin of beef
3 tablespoons olive oil
2 tablespoons harissa paste
from a jar or tube (see introduction)
2 tablespoons Greek-style yoghurt

1.5kg (3lb) sweet potatoes, cut into
wedges
freshly ground black pepper

steamed green beans, to serve

what you do

Preheat the oven to 190°C/375°F/Gas Mark 5.

Cut the top third off the garlic bulb so that the cloves can be squeezed out easily once cooked. Wrap tightly in foil and roast for 30 minutes or until the bulb feels soft when lightly squeezed. Remove from the oven and leave until cool enough to handle, then squeeze the garlic pulp into a bowl. Add one tablespoon of the olive oil with the harissa paste and yoghurt and mix to a smooth paste.

Place the beef in a shallow non-metallic dish. Rub the harissa mixture all over the meat, then cover with clingfilm and chill overnight or leave to stand at room temperature for 2-3 hours if time is short.

If the beef has been chilled overnight, bring it back to room temperature before cooking.

Preheat the oven to 240°C/475°F/Gas Mark 9.

Put the beef in a small roasting tin and season lightly with pepper. Toss the sweet potatoes in the rest of the olive oil and season lightly with pepper, then tip into a separate roasting tin. Place the beef on the bottom shelf of the oven and immediately turn the oven down to 200°C/400°F/Gas Mark 6. Cook for 1 hour for medium well done. If you prefer your beef medium rare, take it out 5-10 minutes earlier. For well done, leave it in for another 10-15 minutes.

Pop the sweet potatoes onto the top shelf of the oven for the last 15-20 minutes of the cooking time.

Remove the beef from the oven and transfer to a warm platter, then leave to rest in a warm place for 10 minutes. Leave the sweet potatoes roasting until cooked through and lightly charred, tossing occasionally to ensure they cook evenly.

Carve the beef into thin slices and arrange on plates with the roasted sweet potato wedges and some green beans to serve.

typical nutritional content – *per portion*			
Energy Kcal (Calories)	333	Salt (g)	0.5
Fat (g)	10.3	Sugars (g)	8.8
of which saturates (g)	3.5		

pot-roasted meatloaf with haricot beans and tomatoes

This is a great dish that all the family will enjoy and it can be prepared well in advance, ready to be popped into the oven. If you're not keen on the idea of the beans, just leave them out. Alternatively, you could stir the sauce into some pasta or serve with jacket potatoes.

Preparation time: 15 minutes • Cooking time: 1 hour 5 minutes • *Serves 6-8*

what you need

2 tablespoons olive oil
2 onions, finely chopped
3 celery sticks, peeled and finely chopped
½ teaspoon ground cumin
½ teaspoon ground coriander
600g (1lb 5oz) lean minced beef
1 large egg
100g (4oz) fresh soft brown breadcrumbs
1 teaspoon fresh thyme, chopped
2 garlic cloves, finely chopped

1 tablespoon fresh sage, chopped
1 red chilli, seeded and finely chopped (wear rubber gloves)
2 x 400g (14oz) tins chopped tomatoes
400g (14oz) tin haricot beans, drained and rinsed
3 rindless streaky bacon rashers, halved
freshly ground black pepper

purple sprouting broccoli, to serve (green broccoli would also work very well)

what you do

Preheat the oven to 230°C/450°F/Gas Mark 8.

Heat half the olive oil in a frying-pan and sauté two-thirds of the onions and two-thirds of the celery for 5 minutes until softened. Stir in the cumin and coriander and cook for another minute, stirring.

Tip the onion mixture into a bowl and add the minced beef, egg, breadcrumbs and thyme. Using your hands, mix well to combine and then mould into a rugby-ball shape. Place in a small roasting tin and put in the oven. Reduce the oven temperature to 200°C/400°F/Gas Mark 6 and roast for 40 minutes.

Meanwhile, make the sauce. Heat the rest of the olive oil in a frying-pan and sauté the remaining onions and celery with garlic, sage and chilli for about 5 minutes until softened but not browned. Season generously with black pepper. Stir in the tomatoes and bring to the boil, then reduce the heat and simmer gently for 10 minutes until slightly reduced in volume and thickened. Fold in the haricot beans.

Remove the meatloaf from the oven and drain off the excess fat, then spoon the tomato sauce around. Lay the slices of bacon over the top of the meatloaf and return to the oven for another 15 minutes or until the meatloaf is cooked through, the bacon is golden brown and the haricot beans are bubbling.

Serve straight to the table with a bowl of purple sprouting broccoli and allow everyone to help themselves.

typical nutritional content – *per portion*			
Energy Kcal (Calories)	307	Salt (g)	0.8
Fat (g)	13.7	Sugars (g)	6.5
of which saturates (g)	4.5		

spaghetti bolognese

★ RECIPE BY Mikey Graham *Singer-songwriter*

There's no doubt that making an authentic bolognese sauce is well worth the effort. I often make a large quantity so that I can freeze it in smaller batches.

Preparation time: 10 minutes · Cooking time: 1 hour 5 minutes · *Serves 4*

what you need

1 tablespoon olive oil
1 onion, finely chopped
1 small carrot, finely diced
1 celery stick, finely diced
1 garlic clove, finely chopped
½ teaspoon fresh thyme, chopped
1 bay leaf

350g (12oz) lean minced beef
1 tablespoon tomato purée
400g (14oz) tin chopped tomatoes
350g (12oz) dried spaghetti
freshly ground black pepper
Parmesan cheese shavings, to garnish

what you do

Heat a large, heavy-based pan. Add the oil and tip in the onion, carrot, celery, garlic, thyme and bay leaf. Cook for 6-8 minutes until the vegetables have softened and browned a little, stirring occasionally.

Add the minced beef to the pan and mix until well combined, then sauté until well browned, breaking up any lumps with a wooden spoon. Stir in the tomato purée and continue to cook for another minute or two, stirring. Add the tomatoes, season lightly with pepper and bring to the boil, then reduce the heat to the lowest setting and simmer for 1 hour until the beef is tender and the sauce has slightly reduced in volume.

Bring a large pan of water to the boil. Add the spaghetti. Stir once and then cook for 8-10 minutes or according to the instructions on the packet until the pasta is just tender but still has a little bite. Drain and then return to the pan. Add the bolognese sauce and toss until well combined.

Divide among warmed wide-rimmed serving bowls. Scatter the Parmesan shavings over to serve.

typical nutritional content – *per portion*			
Energy Kcal (Calories)	523	Salt (g)	0.04
Fat (g)	13.7	Sugars (g)	9.1
of which saturates (g)	4.5		

teriyaki steak

★ RECIPE BY Martina Stanley *Actress*, FAIR CITY

I'm not a big meat-eater and cannot cook a steak to save my life, but this quick and easy stir-fry is one of my favourites. Although fillet steak is expensive, the flavour and texture make it well worth the money. Here I've served it with noodles, but I also like it with rice or a slice of multi-seed brown bread – simply delicious!

Preparation time: 10 mins + 1 hr marinating • Cooking time: 10 mins • *Serves 4*

what you need

350g (12oz) fillet steak, trimmed
2 tablespoons teriyaki sauce
1 tablespoon sunflower oil
1 teaspoon sesame oil
1 large shallot, finely minced
2 garlic cloves, finely minced

2 red peppers, seeded and thinly sliced
100g (4oz) baby spinach leaves

egg or soba noodles, to serve (optional)

what you do

Cut the fillet steak into 1cm (½in) slices and then into thin strips. Place in a shallow non-metallic dish and stir in the teriyaki sauce. Cover with clingfilm and set aside for an hour to marinate – overnight in the fridge is fine too.

Heat a wok over a high heat until very hot and then add the sunflower oil and sesame oil and swirl up the sides. Tip in the shallot and garlic and stir-fry for 20 seconds.

Add the red pepper and marinated steak and stir-fry for another 2-3 minutes until just tender and lightly golden. Remove from the heat and fold in the spinach so that the heat of the dish just wilts it down.

Serve at once in warmed Oriental-style bowls, with noodles if liked.

typical nutritional content – *per portion*			
Energy Kcal (Calories)	406	Salt (g)	1.7
Fat (g)	10.8	Sugars (g)	7.4
of which saturates (g)	3.2		

veal marsala

★ *RECIPE BY* Marty Whelan *Radio and Television Presenter*

This is a recipe I often cook at home. It must be the Italian in me trying to get out. I used to look like a hitman – now I'm beginning to look like a don, whatever that means! Irish veal is now becoming more readily available – but if you don't wish to use veal, pork works well too. Veal needs very little cooking but this dish is good enough to grace any dinner-party table. It's also a great way of using Marsala wine that you may have picked up on your travels. I like it with a little Italian bread to mop up all the delicious juices.

Preparation time: 5 minutes • Cooking time: 30 minutes • *Serves 4*

what you need

12 medium mushrooms, sliced
2 tablespoons olive oil
8 x 50g (2oz) thin rose veal escalopes
4 spring onions, finely chopped
5 tablespoons sweet Marsala wine
120ml (4fl oz) beef stock

1 tablespoon fresh basil, shredded
1 tablespoon butter, softened

egg tagliatelle and steamed long-stem broccoli, to serve

what you do

Bring a small pan of water to the boil, tip in the mushrooms for 2 minutes, then drain.

Heat the olive oil in a large heavy-based frying-pan over medium heat and sauté the veal escalopes for 2-3 minutes on each side until nicely browned – you may have to do this in batches depending on the size of your pan. Transfer to a warmed plate, cover in tinfoil and keep warm.

Reduce the heat and add the spring onions to the residue left in the frying-pan. Sauté for 1-2 minutes until they are softening and then add the mushrooms and sauté for another 2-3 minutes.

Return the veal to the frying-pan and pour in the Marsala wine with the beef stock, then add basil and butter. Bring to the boil, then reduce the heat to low. Cover and simmer for 6-8 minutes or until the sauce has slightly reduced in volume and thickened.

Arrange two pieces of veal on each warmed plate with the egg tagliatelle and steamed broccoli to serve.

typical nutritional content – *per portion*			
Energy Kcal (Calories)	456	Salt (g)	0.3
Fat (g)	13.6	Sugars (g)	2.2
of which saturates (g)	4.1		

beef vindaloo with saffron rice

If you like a hot curry, then you're going to like this dish! A vindaloo is the hottest curry you can get so, if you don't like it really hot, reduce the amount of curry paste to suit your taste. There are now numerous brands of vindaloo curry paste sold in jars.

Preparation time: 15 minutes • Cooking time: 2 hours 15 minutes • *Serves 6-8*

what you need

For the beef vindaloo
2 tablespoons sunflower oil
2 onions, thinly sliced
4 garlic cloves, finely chopped
5cm (2in) piece fresh root ginger, peeled and finely chopped
2 red chillies, seeded and finely chopped (wear rubber gloves)
900g (2lb) stewing beef (such as rib or chuck), cut into 2.5cm (1in) cubes
4 tablespoons vindaloo curry paste
400g (14oz) tin chopped tomatoes
4 tablespoons red wine vinegar
1 teaspoon sugar (optional)

For the saffron rice
1 teaspoon saffron threads
knob of butter
350g (12oz) basmati rice
6 green cardamom pods, cracked
natural yoghurt and fresh coriander leaves, to garnish

what you do

To make the beef vindaloo, heat the oil in a large heavy-based pan and add the onions, garlic, ginger and chillies. Cook for 8-10 minutes until softened and just beginning to turn golden. Add the beef and the vindaloo paste. Stir well until everything is evenly coated and then add 200ml (7fl oz) of water with the tomatoes, vinegar and sugar (if using). Bring to the boil, stirring until well combined. Then reduce the heat, cover with a lid and simmer for 1½-2 hours until the beef is tender but still holding its shape, stirring occasionally to ensure it doesn't stick to the bottom of the pan.

To prepare the saffron rice, place the saffron threads into a small bowl and pour a little boiling water over and leave to infuse. In a large heavy-based saucepan with a lid, heat the butter. When it's just starting to foam, tip in the rice and cardamom. Stir the rice for 2 minutes over a medium heat. Pour enough boiling water over to cover the rice by 2.5cm (1in), bring to a simmer and put on the lid. Allow to cook for 5 minutes then pour in the saffron including the water it has been soaking in. Replace the lid and continue to cook for a further 5 minutes or until the rice is just cooked but retains some bite.

Spoon the beef vindaloo onto warmed plates with the saffron rice and add dollops of natural yoghurt and a good scattering of coriander leaves to serve.

typical nutritional content – *per portion*			
Energy Kcal (Calories)	409	Salt (g)	0.5
Fat (g)	13.2	Sugars (g)	5.7
of which saturates (g)	4.2		

roast fillet of beef with roasted balsamic beetroot

★ *RECIPE BY* Nicky Byrne *Singer,* WESTLIFE

I often serve this dish up to my family and friends for dinner parties or a special occasion. You can buy creamed horseradish in jars from most major supermarkets or you can use one tablespoon of fresh horseradish root (grated) for this recipe.

Preparation time: 10 mins · Cooking time: 55 mins + 10 mins resting · *Serves 6*

what you need

100g (4oz) half-fat crème fraîche
2 tablespoons creamed horseradish
(from a jar) or 1 tablespoon fresh
horseradish root, grated
1 tablespoon Dijon mustard
1½ teaspoons fresh lemon juice
pinch of caster sugar
675g (1½lb) beef fillet (preferably cut
from the thick end)

3 tablespoons olive oil
6 large fresh whole beetroot
3 tablespoons balsamic vinegar
1 teaspoon cumin seeds
freshly ground black pepper

rocket salad, to serve

what you do

To make the horseradish cream, place the crème fraîche in a bowl and stir in the creamed horseradish (or freshly grated horseradish root) with the mustard, lemon juice and caster sugar. Stir until well blended. Spoon into a serving bowl, cover with clingfilm and chill until needed.

Allow the beef fillet to come to room temperature before cooking.

Preheat the oven to 200°C/400°F/Gas Mark 6.

Rub the beef all over with one tablespoon of the olive oil, then season lightly with pepper. Heat a heavy-based frying-pan (ovenproof if possible). Cook the beef fillet over a high heat, turning until all sides are golden brown; this should take about 6 minutes in total.

Peel the beetroot and cut each one into eight wedges. Tip into a roasting tin, then drizzle the vinegar over them. Sprinkle the cumin seeds on top and the remaining two tablespoons of olive oil. Roast for 25-30 minutes until tender but retaining a bite, turning occasionally.

Transfer the seared beef in its ovenproof frying-pan to the oven (or place in a small roasting tin). Roast for 15 minutes per 450g (1lb) for medium rare. This means that a joint this size will take approximately 22 minutes. Add an extra 15 minutes if you prefer your beef well done. Remove from the oven and allow to rest in a warm place for 10 minutes before carving into thin slices.

Arrange the beef fillet on warmed plates with the balsamic beetroot and some of the rocket salad. Serve with the dish of horseradish cream on the side.

typical nutritional content – *per portion*			
Energy Kcal (Calories)	275	Salt (g)	0.6
Fat (g)	15.8	Sugars (g)	7.1
of which saturates (g)	5.7		

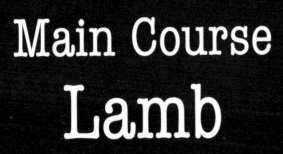

Main Course
Lamb

lamb chops
with garlic and lemon

This recipe would also work well with any type of lamb leg steaks or chump chops. The longer you can marinate the meat, the better the flavour, so it is well worth preparing in advance.

Preparation time: 5 mins + 20 mins marinating

Cooking time: 15 mins + couple of mins resting • *Serves 4*

what you need

2 tablespoons olive oil
4 garlic cloves, cut into slivers
rind of 1 lemon
1 large sprig fresh thyme
8 x 50g (2oz) lamb cutlets, well trimmed

2 heaped tablespoons redcurrant jelly
freshly ground black pepper

steamed baby new potatoes tossed in a little chopped fresh parsley and French beans, to serve

what you do

Place the olive oil in a shallow non-metallic dish and add the garlic and lemon rind. Break up the thyme into small sprigs and scatter on top, then season lightly with pepper. Add the lamb cutlets, turning to coat, then set aside for at least 20 minutes, or up to 24 hours, covered with clingfilm in the fridge.

When you are ready to cook, light the barbecue or preheat a griddle pan or large frying-pan until very hot. Brush the excess marinade off the lamb and put the chops on the barbecue on medium-hot coals or on the griddle or frying pan. Cook for 6-8 minutes until cooked through and tender, turning once. Remove from the heat and leave to rest for a couple of minutes.

Arrange the lamb cutlets on warmed plates with the baby new potatoes and some French beans. Add a spoonful of redcurrant jelly to each one to serve.

typical nutritional content – *per portion*			
Energy Kcal (Calories)	412	Salt (g)	0.2
Fat (g)	18.5	Sugars (g)	10.7
of which saturates (g)	7.0		

grilled lamb pittas with mint salad

★ *RECIPE BY* Neven Maguire MacNean House & Restaurant *Blacklion, Co Cavan*

These lamb pittas are wonderfully succulent and also would be perfect to cook on the barbecue. As an alternative, try using minced chicken or turkey.

Preparation time: 10 mins + 30 mins chilling • **Cooking time:** 15 mins • *Serves 4*

what you need

For the lamb pittas
675g (1½lb) lean minced lamb
2 tablespoons fresh flat-leaf parsley, chopped
1 tablespoon fresh mint, chopped
1 small onion, finely chopped
1 garlic clove, crushed
1 egg
1 tablespoon sweet chilli sauce
4 wholemeal pitta breads
25g (1oz) rocket

For the mint salad
3 ripe vine tomatoes, sliced
1 red onion, thinly sliced
1 tablespoon fresh mint, chopped
1 tablespoon extra virgin olive oil
1 tablespoon fresh lemon juice
freshly ground black pepper

what you do

Place the minced lamb in a large bowl with the parsley, mint, onion, garlic, egg and sweet chilli sauce. Mix together until well combined and then divide the mixture into twelve equal portions. Using wetted hands, shape into patties and then arrange on a baking tray. Cover with clingfilm and chill for 30 minutes to firm up.

Preheat the grill and the oven to 160°C/325°F/Gas Mark 3.

Arrange the patties on a grill rack and cook for 10 minutes or until cooked through and golden brown, turning once. Meanwhile, wrap the pitta breads in tinfoil and place in the oven for 5 minutes to warm through.

To make the mint salad, place the tomatoes, red onion, mint, olive oil and lemon juice in a bowl. Season lightly with pepper and toss gently to coat.

Remove the pitta breads from the oven and split open the pockets, then fill each one with the rocket, some mint salad and three of the lamb burgers.

Arrange on warmed plates to serve.

typical nutritional content – *per portion*			
Energy Kcal (Calories)	512	Salt (g)	1.2
Fat (g)	18.1	Sugars (g)	6.3
of which saturates (g)	1.0		

butterflied leg of lamb with puy lentil salad

To barbecue the lamb instead of roasting, place over medium-hot coals for about 40 minutes for medium rare, turning occasionally. Either way it is perfect served with this lentil and rocket salad which can be made well in advance and kept in the fridge.

Preparation time: 15 mins + 2 hrs marinating • Cooking time: 45 mins • *Serves 6*

what you need

For the lamb
2kg (4½lb) leg of lamb, boned and butterflied (ask your butcher)
4 garlic cloves, roughly chopped
1 tablespoon fresh oregano
handful fresh mint leaves
1 tablespoon anchovy fillets
finely grated rind and juice of 1 lemon
2 tablespoons olive oil

For the puy lentil and rocket salad
225g (8oz) puy lentils
1 tablespoon olive oil
2 shallots, finely chopped
50g (2oz) sun-dried tomatoes preserved in olive oil, drained
50g (2oz) wild rocket, any tough stalks picked out
freshly ground black pepper

what you do

Make some deep incisions in the lamb with a sharp knife and then place in a large sealable bag. Blend together the garlic, oregano, mint, anchovies, lemon rind and juice and olive oil to form a thick paste. Season lightly with pepper and then pour into the bag and close. 'Massage' the lamb ensuring it is well covered with the paste and then leave to marinate in the fridge for at least 2 hours but preferably overnight. Massage well occasionally. Remove from fridge and bring to room temperature before cooking.

Preheat the oven to 220°C/425°F/Gas Mark 7.

Place the lamb on a rack above a roasting tin. Roast for 10 minutes, then turn down the oven temperature to 200°C/400°F/Gas Mark 6 and continue to cook for another 30 minutes for medium rare, adding another 15 minutes for medium well done.

Meanwhile, to make the lentil salad, rinse the lentils in a sieve under cold running water, then place in a pan with 600ml (1 pint) of water. Bring to the boil and then reduce the heat and simmer for 15-20 minutes or until just tender but still with a little bite. Drain well. Heat the olive oil in a pan and sauté the shallots for 4-5 minutes until softened but not browned. Tip into a salad bowl and stir in the cooked lentils with the sun-dried tomatoes.

Remove the lamb from the oven and transfer it onto a board, then cover with a sheet of foil and leave to rest for 10 minutes.

When the lentils have cooled to room temperature, gently fold in the rocket and season lightly with pepper.

Carve the lamb into thin slices and serve with some of the salad.

typical nutritional content – *per portion*			
Energy Kcal (Calories)	721	Salt (g)	1.2
Fat (g)	36.5	Sugars (g)	1.2
of which saturates (g)	13.0		

fragrant lamb skewers with tabbouleh salad

This is a classic Middle Eastern salad made with cracked wheat, also known as bulgur or burghul wheat. You'll find it in health shops or usually alongside the dried pulses and beans in the supermarket. The salad is really colourful and goes very well with fragrant lamb skewers.

Preparation time: 15 mins + 45 mins soaking • **Cooking time:** 15 mins • *Serves 4*

what you need

For the lamb skewers
500g (1lb 2oz) boneless leg of lamb chops
1 tablespoon olive oil
1 teaspoon each ground ginger, cumin, coriander and turmeric
juice and grated rind of ½ lemon
1 small bunch of fresh coriander
2 tablespoons Greek-style yoghurt

For the tabbouleh salad
100g (4oz) bulgur wheat
juice of ½ lemon
2 tablespoons extra-virgin olive oil
3 ripe plum tomatoes, halved, seeded and diced
15g (½oz) fresh flat-leaf parsley leaves, roughly chopped
1 bunch spring onions, trimmed and finely chopped
freshly ground black pepper

what you do

To prepare the lamb, trim well and cut into bite-sized pieces. Place the olive oil, ginger, cumin, coriander, turmeric, lemon rind and juice, fresh coriander and yoghurt into a liquidiser and blend to form a smooth paste. Place the lamb in a shallow non-metallic dish and fold in the spice paste. Cover with clingfilm and chill for at least 20 minutes or overnight in the fridge to allow the flavours to develop if time allows.

To make the tabbouleh salad, place the bulgur wheat in a bowl and pour enough cold water over to cover. Set aside for 45 minutes or according to packet instructions until just tender, then tip into a sieve and rinse well under cold running water. Drain well and tip into a bowl.

Meanwhile, make the dressing. Place the lemon juice in a screw-topped jar, season lightly with pepper, then shake well. Add the olive oil and shake again until well combined.

Add the tomatoes to the drained bulgur wheat with the parsley and spring onions. Stir until well combined and then mix the dressing through the bulgur mixture. Season lightly with pepper. Set aside at room temperature, covered with clingfilm, for up to 2 hours, to allow the flavours to develop.

To serve, preheat the grill to a medium heat or light a barbecue. Then grill the lamb skewers or barbecue them on medium-hot coals for 8-10 minutes, turning now and then, until lightly browned and cooked through.

Arrange on warmed plates with the tabbouleh salad to serve.

typical nutritional content – *per portion*			
Energy Kcal (Calories)	248	Salt (g)	0.3
Fat (g)	15.4	Sugars (g)	1.2
of which saturates (g)	6.3		

lamb shanks with roasted vegetables

★ *RECIPE BY* Tim O'Sullivan RENVYLE HOUSE HOTEL *Renvyle, Connemara, Co Galway*

This dish could almost be called an Irish stew. Indeed, it is a wonderful alternative. Ask your butcher to trim off any visible fat from the shanks and to remove the knuckles. It is worth noting that lamb shanks can vary in size, depending on the time of year.

Preparation time: 10 minutes • **Cooking time:** 2 hours 45 minutes • *Serves 4*

what you need

4 x 200g (7oz) lamb shanks
1 tablespoon vegetable oil
4 fresh rosemary sprigs
2 garlic cloves, finely chopped
250g (9oz) carrots, cut into chunks
250g (9oz) parsnips, trimmed and cut into chunks

250g (9oz) turnips, trimmed and cut into small chunks
8 shallots, peeled
1 tablespoon fresh flat-leaf parsley, chopped, plus extra to garnish
1 tablespoon fresh chives, snipped
freshly ground black pepper

what you do

Preheat the oven to 170°C/325°F/Gas Mark 3.

Heat the oil in a large pot over a high heat. Fry the lamb shanks in batches until nicely browned on all sides. Transfer them to a plate while you cook the remainder. Put the lamb, rosemary, and garlic into an oven-proof dish with a lid. Add 300ml (½ pint) of water and season lightly with pepper. Cover tightly with foil and then with the lid. Cook in the oven for 90 minutes.

Remove the lamb shanks from the oven and take off the lid and foil. Stir in the carrots, parsnips, turnips and shallots and cook for another 45 minutes to 1 hour or until the lamb shanks are tender and almost falling off the bone.

Transfer the lamb shanks to a warmed dish with the vegetables and return the pot to the hob. Skim off any visible fat from the top of the juice. Boil the juice quickly for 5-6 minutes or until it has a light sauce consistency. Remove from the heat and add the parsley and chives.

Warm four large plates. Place a shank of lamb in the centre of each, surrounded with vegetables. Coat with the sauce and garnish with the parsley to serve.

typical nutritional content – *per portion*			
Energy Kcal (Calories)	271	Salt (g)	0.3
Fat (g)	12.3	Sugars (g)	13.0
of which saturates (g)	4.3		

lamb stew with turnip and pearl barley

This is not a lamb stew in the traditional sense but is just as delicious. It uses shoulder of lamb that has been well trimmed so is much less fatty than the gigot chops that are normally used. The potatoes are added on top for the last 40 minutes of cooking so that they become nice and golden.

Preparation time: 15 minutes • **Cooking time:** 1 hour 45 minutes • *Serves 6*

what you need

2 tablespoons plain flour
675g (1½lb) shoulder of lamb, well trimmed and cut into bite-sized pieces
2 tablespoons pearl barley
1 teaspoon fresh thyme, chopped
1 small onion, sliced
1 large leek, sliced

2 large carrots, sliced
100g (4oz) turnip, cut into cubes
about 600ml (1 pint) chicken stock
675g (1½lb) even-sized potatoes, peeled
1 tablespoon sunflower oil
freshly ground black pepper

what you do

Preheat the oven to 180°C/350°F/Gas Mark 4.

Place the flour in a shallow dish and season lightly with pepper, then use to coat the diced lamb. Arrange half of the lamb in the bottom of a round casserole dish with a lid and scatter half of the pearl barley over, then add a sprinkling of thyme. Layer up the onion, leek, carrots and turnip and finish with the rest of the pearl barley, then add another sprinkling of thyme. Arrange the remaining lamb on top to cover the vegetables completely and sprinkle the remaining thyme over.

Pour enough chicken stock to just come up above the last layer of lamb. Cover the casserole with a lid and place in the oven for about 1 hour until the lamb and vegetables are almost tender and the stock has thickened slightly.

Meanwhile, place the potatoes in a pan of boiling water and bring to the boil, then simmer for 10 minutes. Drain in a colander and set aside for 5 minutes until cool enough to handle. Slice the potatoes lengthways into 1cm (½in) thick slices and lay them in a slightly overlapping layer on top of the stew. Brush lightly with the sunflower oil. Return the stew to the oven and cook for another 40 minutes until the potatoes are cooked through and nicely golden. Serve straight to the table so that everyone can help themselves.

typical nutritional content – *per portion*			
Energy Kcal (Calories)	317	Salt (g)	0.5
Fat (g)	11.2	Sugars (g)	5.6
of which saturates (g)	0.4		

lamb tagine with green couscous

This tagine may seem like it's got a lot of ingredients but the results are worth it. Ask your butcher to prepare the lamb for you as this can save a good deal of time. For a more fragrant and pungent dish, the lamb can be covered in clingfilm and marinated in the fridge for up to 24 hours to allow the spices to penetrate the meat.

Preparation time: 10 minutes • Cooking time: 1 hour 40 minutes • *Serves 6-8*

what you need

1 tablespoon paprika
1 teaspoon each ground coriander and turmeric, cinnamon and cumin
900g (2lb) lamb stewing pieces, well trimmed
1 large onion, roughly chopped
2 garlic cloves, finely chopped
2.5cm (1in) piece fresh root ginger, peeled and chopped
2 tablespoons olive oil
700ml (1¼ pints) chicken stock

400g (14oz) tin chopped tomatoes
1 tablespoon clear honey
225g (8oz) couscous
juice of 1 lemon
2 tablespoons each of fresh mixed flat-leaf parsley and mint, chopped
cracked black pepper
Greek-style yoghurt and fresh coriander leaves, to garnish

what you do

Heat a large heavy-based pan with a lid. Mix together the paprika, coriander, turmeric, cinnamon, cumin and 1 teaspoon of pepper in a large bowl. Add the lamb and using your hands rub in the spices. Add 1 tablespoon of the olive oil to the heated pan and quickly cook half of the spiced lamb until brown. Transfer to a plate and repeat with the remaining lamb.

Meanwhile, place the onion, garlic and ginger in a food processor or hand-blender and pulse until finely minced. Add the onion mixture to the residue left in the pan from cooking the lamb and sauté for 3-4 minutes until well softened and browned from the spices left in the bottom of the pan.

Pour 300ml (½ pint) of the stock into the pan and stir in the tomatoes and honey. Add the lamb, bring to the boil, season lightly with pepper and simmer for about 1½ hours or until the lamb is completely tender but still holding its shape and the sauce has thickened and reduced in volume.

Place the couscous in a bowl and add the remaining tablespoon of the oil and the lemon juice, stirring to ensure all the grains are completely coated. Heat the remaining 400ml (14fl oz) of stock in a small pan and season generously with black pepper. Pour the seasoned stock over the couscous and allow to sit in a warm place for 6-8 minutes until all the liquid has been absorbed.

To serve, stir the parsley and mint into the couscous and reheat gently in a pan. Arrange on warmed plates with the lamb. Garnish each plate with a dollop of the Greek yoghurt and coriander leaves to serve.

typical nutritional content – *per portion*			
Energy Kcal (Calories)	410	Salt (g)	0.4
Fat (g)	14.4	Sugars (g)	6.3
of which saturates (g)	1.7		

seared lamb with chutney

Leave any leftover chutney to cool completely, then store in an airtight container for up to 3-4 days in the fridge. It is delicious with a cheese sandwich or slices of cooked ham and a fresh green salad.

Preparation time: 10 mins • **Cooking time:** 30 mins + 15 mins cooling • *Serves 6*

what you need

6 x 125g (4½oz) lamb loin chops or leg steaks

For the aubergine chutney
2 tablespoons olive oil
1 large aubergine, cut into 1cm (½in) cubes
1 onion, finely chopped
1 celery stick, finely chopped
2.5cm (1in) piece fresh root ginger, peeled and finely chopped

1 teaspoon medium curry powder
1 tablespoon tomato purée
1 tablespoon clear honey
2 tablespoons red wine vinegar
25g (1oz) pine nuts
25g (1oz) raisins
4 tablespoons fresh coriander or flat-leaf parsley, roughly chopped
freshly ground black pepper

salad, to serve

what you do

Heat the olive oil in a large frying-pan. Add the aubergine, season lightly with pepper and sauté for 8-10 minutes until cooked through and tender. Add the onion to the pan with the celery and ginger and cook for another 4-5 minutes or until all the vegetables are softened but not browned.

Sprinkle the curry powder over the aubergine mixture, then stir in the tomato purée and cook for 2-3 minutes, stirring frequently. Add the honey and vinegar with 6 tablespoons of water, stirring to combine, then simmer gently for another 5 minutes or until well reduced in volume and thickened.

Meanwhile, heat a frying-pan over a medium heat. Add the pine nuts and cook for a few minutes until toasted, tossing occasionally. Add to the aubergine mixture with the raisins and coriander or parsley. Simmer gently for another couple of minutes to allow the flavours to combine. Transfer to a bowl and set aside at room temperature to cool.

Trim any visible fat from the meat and, when almost ready to serve, arrange on the grill rack and cook for 3-4 minutes on each side until cooked through and tender. Remove from the heat and leave in a warm place for a few minutes to allow the meat to rest. Arrange the rested lamb on warmed plates with small mounds of the aubergine chutney. Add some salad to serve.

typical nutritional content – *per portion*			
Energy Kcal (Calories)	282	Salt (g)	0.1
Fat (g)	15.7	Sugars (g)	9.4
of which saturates (g)	0.8		

Main Course
Vegetarian

chickpea and cauliflower curry with flatbread

This curry is also a worthy partner to steamed basmati rice or shop-bought chapatis and goes equally well with grilled or roasted spicy meat dishes. The flatbreads can literally be made in minutes, just don't make them too far in advance or they will begin to harden.

Preparation time: 15 minutes ● Cooking time: 30 minutes ● *Serves 4*

what you need

For the curry
1 tablespoon sunflower oil
1 onion, thinly sliced
2 garlic cloves, crushed
2.5cm (1in) piece fresh root ginger, peeled and grated
1 green chilli, seeded and finely chopped (wear rubber gloves)
2 teaspoons hot curry powder (such as Madras)
300ml (½ pint) vegetable stock
400g (14oz) tin chopped tomatoes
225g (8oz) small cauliflower florets
400g (14oz) tin chickpeas, drained and rinsed

225g (8oz) baby spinach
2 tablespoons Greek-style yoghurt

For the flatbreads
4 tablespoons Greek-style yoghurt
1 egg, lightly beaten
225g (8oz) self-raising flour, plus extra for dusting
1 green chilli, seeded and finely chopped (wear rubber gloves)
2 tablespoons fresh coriander, chopped
a little sunflower oil
freshly ground black pepper

what you do

Heat the sunflower oil in a pan (use one with a lid as you will need the cover later), then sauté the onion for about 5 minutes or until softened and just beginning to go brown. Tip in the garlic, ginger and chilli and continue to cook for 1 minute, stirring. Stir in the curry powder and cook for another minute, then stir in the stock and tomatoes and bring to a simmer. Add the cauliflower, cover and simmer for 15-20 minutes or until tender but still with a little bite.

To make the flatbreads, heat a large non-stick flat griddle or frying-pan. In a bowl, mix the yoghurt with enough warm water to make 120ml (4fl oz) of liquid, then stir in the beaten egg. Sift the flour into a bowl with a little black pepper. Make a well in the centre and add the yoghurt mixture with the chilli and coriander. Quickly mix to a soft but not sticky dough.

Turn the dough out on to a floured work surface and knead for about 30 seconds until smooth. Cut into four and roll out each piece to an oval shape that is 0.5cm (¼in) thick. Add a thin film of oil to the heated pan and cook one at a time for 4-5 minutes on each side until cooked through and lightly golden. Wrap in a clean tea towel until needed.

Stir the chickpeas and spinach into the cauliflower mixture and cook for a few minutes until heated through and the spinach has wilted.

Divide the curry into warmed bowls set on plates and add a spoonful of yoghurt to each one. Place the flatbreads on the side to serve.

typical nutritional content – *per portion*			
Energy Kcal (Calories)	452	Salt (g)	2.0
Fat (g)	13.1	Sugars (g)	9.3
of which saturates (g)	5.8		

tomato and basil omelette

Omelettes are so easy to make and a great meal that all of the family will enjoy. Don't be tempted to over-beat the egg mixture, as it will spoil the texture. Of course, you could put in any filling that you fancy.

Preparation time: 10 mins • Cooking time: 15 mins + 5 mins resting • Serves 6

what you need

2 tablespoons sunflower oil
1 onion, chopped
5 vine-ripened tomatoes, peeled,
seeded and chopped
6 large eggs
4 tablespoons low-fat cream cheese
or crème fraîche
50g (2oz) freshly grated Parmesan
cheese (vegetarian if necessary)

6 fresh basil leaves
2 teaspoons fresh chives, snipped into
little pieces
freshly ground black pepper

salad, to serve

what you do

Heat a large frying-pan with a base approximately 25cm (10in) in diameter and then add half of the oil. Add the onion and cook for a few minutes until softened but not browned. Add the tomatoes and continue to cook until all the excess liquid has been removed but the tomatoes are still just holding their shape. Tip into a bowl and set aside.

Preheat the grill to a medium heat. Wipe the frying-pan with kitchen paper and return to the heat. Place the eggs in a bowl with the cream cheese or crème fraîche and most of the Parmesan, keeping a little to garnish. Tear in the basil and stir in the chives. Season lightly with pepper and beat lightly until just combined.

Heat the rest of the oil in the frying-pan. As it stops sizzling pour in the egg mixture, then tip in the onion and tomato mixture, mixing gently with a spoon or fork to spread evenly. Sprinkle the remaining Parmesan on top and cook for five minutes over a low heat or until the base is firm and the sides come away easily from the pan.

Place the omelette under the grill and cook gently until lightly browned all over. Remove from the heat and leave to settle in the pan for about 5 minutes, then cut into slices and arrange on plates with plenty of salad to serve.

typical nutritional content – per portion			
Energy Kcal (Calories)	225	Salt (g)	0.4
Fat (g)	17.0	Sugars (g)	4.6
of which saturates (g)	6.3		

focaccia pizza

★ *RECIPE BY* Biddy White Lennon *Food Writer*

This delicious pizza is made using focaccia bread as a base. Of course, if you don't want to go to the bother of making focaccia bread, just buy one and split in half, then simply follow the instructions below.

Preparation time: 30 mins + 1 hr 20 mins rising • Cooking time: 40 mins • *Serves 8*

what you need

For the dough
1 teaspoon fast-action yeast
4 tablespoons extra-virgin olive oil

450g (1lb) strong plain white flour, plus extra for dusting

For the tomato sauce
2 teaspoons olive oil
1 onion, finely chopped
2 garlic cloves, crushed
400g (14oz) tin chopped tomatoes
1 tablespoon tomato purée

For the toppings
100g (4oz) pitted black olives
1 yellow pepper, seeded and thinly sliced
1 small red onion, cut into rings
50g (2oz) mozzarella cheese, grated (vegetarian if necessary)
freshly ground black pepper

salad, to serve

what you do

Mix together the yeast and flour in a large bowl. Make a well in the centre and pour in 300ml (½ pint) of tepid water and two tablespoons of the olive oil. Mix well to achieve a soft dough. Turn the dough out onto a lightly floured surface and knead for 10 minutes until smooth and elastic. Place in a bowl brushed over with oil, cover with clingfilm also brushed over with oil and leave to rise in a warm place for about 1 hour or until doubled in size.

Turn the dough back out onto a lightly floured surface and knead for another 2-3 minutes, then roll out to a large rectangle that is about 1cm (½in) thick. Place on an oiled baking sheet and cover with oiled clingfilm. Leave to rise again for about 20 minutes.

Preheat the oven to 220°C/425°F/Gas Mark 7.

Prick the risen dough all over with a fork. Drizzle again with the rest of the olive oil and bake for about 30 minutes until cooked through and golden brown. Transfer to a wire rack to cool.

To make the tomato sauce, heat the oil in a heavy-based pan. Add the onion and cook gently for a few minutes until softened but not browned. Add the garlic and cook for 1 minute, stirring. Add the tomatoes, tomato purée and season lightly with pepper. Bring to a simmer and cook for about 5 minutes or until nicely reduced in volume and thickened.

Preheat the oven to 200°C/400°F/Gas Mark 6 and preheat the grill to a medium heat. Split the focaccia carefully in two and lightly toast under the grill. Spread the tomato sauce over it, making sure you spread right to the edge. Scatter the olives, yellow pepper and red onion on top and finish with the mozzarella. Place on two baking trays and bake in the oven for 8-10 minutes or until bubbling and lightly golden.

Cut into slices and serve with some salad.

typical nutritional content – *per portion*			
Energy Kcal (Calories)	300	Salt (g)	0.8
Fat (g)	9.8	Sugars (g)	4.9
of which saturates (g)	2.1		

rigatoni pasta with goats' cheese and spinach marinara

★ RECIPE BY Cathal Moran WINEPORT LODGE *Athlone, Co Westmeath*

This recipe is easy enough for everyday eating but good enough to serve to friends. If you haven't got time to make a basil pesto there are some very good shop-bought varieties available.

Preparation time: 15 minutes · Cooking time: 15 minutes · *Serves 4*

what you need

350g (12oz) rigatoni pasta or penne
or fusilli
1 tablespoon olive oil
1 onion, finely chopped
2 garlic cloves, crushed
1 teaspoon fresh thyme, chopped
2 bay leaves
1 teaspoon balsamic vinegar
400g (14oz) tin chopped tomatoes
100g (4oz) baby spinach leaves

1 tablespoon basil pesto
100g (4oz) soft goats' cheese, cut
into cubes (or use Boilie goats' cheese
from a jar)
2 tablespoons pine nuts, toasted
handful fresh basil leaves
freshly ground black pepper

tossed green salad, to serve

what you do

Place the pasta in a large pan of boiling water and cook for 10-12 minutes until tender but still with a little bite, or according to packet instructions.

Meanwhile, place the olive oil in a large frying-pan (or sauté pan) and cook the onion for 2-3 minutes until softened. Add the garlic, thyme and bay leaves and continue to cook over a low heat for another 5 minutes, stirring occasionally. Add the balsamic vinegar and toss until all the ingredients are evenly coated, then sauté until the liquid has completely reduced in volume and formed a nice glaze.

Add the tomatoes to the onion and balsamic mixture and bring to a simmer, then stir in the spinach until just wilted. Stir in the pesto and season with a little pepper. Gently fold in the goats' cheese and remove from the heat.

Drain the cooked pasta and quickly refresh under cold running water, then fold into the sauce.

Divide between serving bowls. Scatter the pine nuts on top and tear the basil over to serve. Have a separate bowl of salad at the table to pass around.

typical nutritional content – *per portion*			
Energy Kcal (Calories)	512	Salt (g)	0.7
Fat (g)	16.2	Sugars (g)	13.7
of which saturates (g)	3.9		

roasted vegetables with tzatziki and couscous

This dish is delicious hot or cold. Try using any combination of Mediterranean vegetables you fancy. However, it's important that the vegetables are not too crowded in the roasting tin, or they'll stew rather than roast.

Preparation time: 15 minutes   Cooking time: 40 minutes   *Serves 4*

what you need

For the roasted vegetables
2 red peppers, seeded and chopped
2 yellow peppers, seeded and chopped
1 large courgette, chopped
1 small aubergine, chopped
1 large red onion, chopped
2 tablespoons olive oil
handful fresh basil leaves

For the tzatziki
¼ cucumber
200g (7oz) Greek-style yoghurt
1 teaspoon chopped fresh mint
1 garlic clove, crushed
pinch of paprika

For the couscous
juice of 1 lemon
175g (6oz) couscous
1 tablespoon chopped fresh flat-leaf parsley
freshly ground black pepper

what you do

Preheat the oven to 230°C/450°F/Gas Mark 8.

Heat a large roasting tin in the oven. Place the red and yellow peppers, courgette, aubergine and red onion in a large bowl and drizzle the olive oil over, tossing to coat evenly. Then tip into the heated roasting tin. Season lightly with black pepper and roast for about 40 minutes or until the vegetables are completely tender and lightly caramelised, tossing from time to time to ensure they cook evenly. About 5 minutes before the vegetables are ready, chop up the basil. Scatter over the vegetables, tossing to combine, then return to the oven to finish cooking.

To make the tzatziki, remove the seeds from the cucumber and then grate very coarsely into a sieve. Set aside to drain for 10 minutes, and then pat dry with kitchen paper. Place the yoghurt in a bowl and stir in the mint and garlic, then fold into the drained cucumber. Season lightly with black pepper and keep covered.

Place the couscous in a large bowl with the lemon juice, stirring gently to combine. Pour 175ml (6fl oz) of boiling water onto the couscous, then stir well, cover and leave to stand for 5 minutes before gently separating the grains with a fork. Season with black pepper to taste and place in a pan to reheat gently, then fold in the parsley.

Divide the couscous between plates and pile the roasted vegetables on top. Add a dollop of the tzatziki to each plate and give a good grinding of black pepper. Serve the remainder of the tzatziki separately in a bowl garnished with a sprinkling of paprika.

typical nutritional content – *per portion*			
Energy Kcal (Calories)	280	Salt (g)	0.1
Fat (g)	11.1	Sugars (g)	15.6
of which saturates (g)	4.0		

fragrant thai pumpkin curry with sticky rice

Thai curries are very quick and easy to prepare, especially now that most supermarkets sell authentic ready-made curry pastes flavoured with chilli, ginger, garlic, lemongrass and spices. Once the jar of paste has been opened, try to use it up within a month as that wonderful fragrant flavour will be lost over time. Sushi rice is the sticky rice that is used to make sushi. You can buy it in a packet in the supermarket beside other rice options.

Preparation time: 15 minutes • Cooking time: 40 minutes • *Serves 6-8*

what you need

1 bunch fresh coriander (roots intact)
4 shallots, chopped
1 garlic clove, chopped
1cm (½in) piece peeled root ginger, chopped
1 red chilli, seeded and chopped (wear rubber gloves)
2 tablespoons Thai red curry paste
400g (14oz) tin coconut milk

1 small pumpkin or a large butternut squash
450ml (¾ pint) vegetable stock
275g (10oz) sushi rice
1 tablespoon Thai fish sauce (nam pla) – optional
juice of 1 lime
4 spring onions, thinly sliced on the diagonal, to garnish

what you do

Remove the leaves from the bunch of coriander and set aside for garnishing. Roughly chop the stems and place in a blender with the shallots, garlic, ginger, chilli, curry paste and two tablespoons of the coconut milk (use the thick creamy coconut milk that settles at the top of the tin). Blend until well combined to a paste consistency.

Peel the pumpkin or butternut squash and cut into quarters, then remove the seeds. Chop the flesh into 2.5cm (1in) chunks – you should end up with about 900g (2lb) in total.

Heat a large pan. Add the paste you've made and stir-fry for 2-3 minutes until cooked through but not browned. Add the pumpkin and continue to stir-fry for another 2-3 minutes until just beginning to brown. Pour in the vegetable stock with the rest of the coconut milk, stirring to combine. Bring to the boil, then reduce the heat and simmer for 25-30 minutes or until the pumpkin is completely tender but still holding its shape.

Meanwhile, make the sticky rice. Rinse the rice thoroughly with running water and place in a pan with 600ml (1 pint) of water. Bring to the boil, then reduce the heat, cover and simmer for 6-8 minutes until all the water is completely absorbed. Turn off the heat and leave the rice to steam for at least another 4-6 minutes until tender – it will sit well for up to 20 minutes with the lid on.

Stir the Thai fish sauce (if using) and lime juice into the curry.

Divide the rice between bowls and ladle in the curry. Garnish with the remaining coriander leaves and the spring onions.

typical nutritional content – *per portion*			
Energy Kcal (Calories)	228	Salt (g)	1.2
Fat (g)	3.0	Sugars (g)	7.2
of which saturates (g)	0.3		

quick wok curry noodles

★ *RECIPE BY* Donal Skehan *Cook, Photographer and Food Writer*

This is real fast food! It's a perfect little recipe that you can pull together using ingredients from your store-cupboard and fridge. The true beauty is that you can adapt it using whatever vegetables you have in the house, so feel free to experiment. It's the addition of curry powder that adds great heat and gives a totally different flavour from any stir-fry you will have cooked before!

Preparation time: 10 mins + 30 mins marinating • Cooking time: 15 mins • *Serves 4*

what you need

4 celery sticks, finely sliced into matchsticks
2 carrots, finely sliced into matchsticks
4 large garlic cloves, minced
5cm (2in) piece root ginger, peeled and finely grated
2 tablespoons oyster sauce (optional)
3 tablespoons dark soy sauce
225g (8oz) Thai rice noodles

2 tablespoons sunflower oil
2 teaspoons medium curry powder
6 spring onions, finely sliced
50g (2oz) bean sprouts
2 teaspoons sesame oil
1 teaspoon toasted sesame seeds (optional)
coriander sprigs to garnish

what you do

Marinate the celery and carrots in a large bowl with the garlic, ginger, oyster sauce (optional) and half of the soy sauce. Cover with clingfilm and place in the fridge for at least 30 minutes.

Soak the noodles in a bowl of boiling water for 8-10 minutes or according to packet instructions. Then stop them cooking by rinsing in cold water. Drain and set aside.

Heat a wok over a high heat and add the sunflower oil, swirling up the sides to coat. Add the marinated vegetables, and stir-fry for 2-3 minutes. Sprinkle in the curry powder and toss through for another 2-3 minutes.

Add the softened noodles with the spring onions, bean sprouts and sesame oil. Toss everything together until it's just combined.

Serve straight away in warmed deep Asian-style bowls scattered with the toasted sesame seeds, if liked, and garnish with the coriander sprigs.

typical nutritional content – *per portion*			
Energy Kcal (Calories)	310	Salt (g)	2.9
Fat (g)	7.6	Sugars (g)	5.2
of which saturates (g)	1.0		

spring vegetable and parmesan risotto

Arborio rice is now readily available. It has the ability to take six times its weight in liquid and benefits from being set aside once it is almost cooked. If using fresh podded peas and/or broad beans, choose ones on the small side that are bright green and plump. If you cannot get fresh peas or beans, use frozen which are just as good. Otherwise asparagus tips or green beans would work well.

Preparation time: 15 minutes • **Cooking time:** 25 minutes • *Serves 4*

what you need

2 tablespoons olive oil
2 leeks, trimmed and diced
2 garlic cloves, crushed
1.2 litres (2 pints) vegetable stock
350g (12oz) arborio (risotto) rice
150ml (¼ pint) white wine
150g (5oz) fresh peas, podded or frozen peas

225g (8oz) broad beans, skins removed, or frozen broad beans
2 tablespoons fresh mixed herbs (such as chives, flat-leaf parsley and basil), chopped
25g (1oz) freshly grated Parmesan cheese (vegetarian if necessary)
freshly ground black pepper

what you do

Heat the oil in a large sauté pan and gently fry the leeks and garlic over a low heat for a few minutes until softened but not browned, stirring occasionally.

Bring the stock to a gentle simmer in a separate pan.

Stir the rice into the leek mixture and cook for 1 minute, stirring until the grains are well coated in oil and almost transparent. Pour in the wine and allow to simmer down for 1 minute, stirring.

Add a ladleful of the simmering stock and cook until it has been completely absorbed, stirring continuously. Continue to add the stock a ladleful at a time, making sure that each time you add the stock the previous amount has already been absorbed.

After 20 minutes the rice should be nearly cooked, so tip the peas and broad beans into the remaining stock for 2 minutes (3-4 minutes if frozen) before adding both the stock and the vegetables to the risotto.

Check that the rice is tender but still with a little bite. Then remove from the heat and stir in the herbs and most of the Parmesan, keeping a little to garnish. Season lightly with pepper.

Spoon the risotto into warmed wide-rimmed bowls and garnish with the rest of the Parmesan and a good grinding of black pepper.

typical nutritional content – *per portion*			
Energy Kcal (Calories)	478	Salt (g)	0.9
Fat (g)	9.0	Sugars (g)	3.8
of which saturates (g)	2.1		

falafel with yoghurt dressing and salad

Try not to use tinned chickpeas for this recipe. It is worth the extra cooking time to cook dried chickpeas yourself. The resulting texture is truly excellent. Serve them with warm pitta bread and crispy salad for an authentic Middle Eastern flavour.

Preparation time: 10 mins + soaking overnight • Cooking time: 35 mins • *Serves 4*

what you need

For the falafel
225g (8oz) dried chickpeas, soaked overnight in water
1 teaspoon ground cumin
1 teaspoon ground coriander
½ teaspoon cayenne pepper
2 garlic cloves, crushed
3 tablespoons fresh flat-leaf parsley, roughly chopped
juice of ½ lemon
1 egg
2 tablespoons olive oil

For the yoghurt dressing
150g (5oz) Greek-style yoghurt
50g (2oz) cucumber, seeded, grated and squeezed dry
1 teaspoon fresh mint, chopped
freshly ground black pepper

To serve
4 wholemeal pitta breads
mixed salad leaves

what you do

Drain the chickpeas and place in a pan, then cover with fresh water and bring to the boil. Boil rapidly for 20 minutes. Drain and place in a food processor with the cumin, coriander, cayenne, garlic, parsley, lemon juice and egg. Season lightly with pepper and blend until very finely chopped but not puréed.

Heat a large heavy-based frying pan. Using wet hands, shape the chickpea mixture into about 16 balls and then flatten slightly into patties. Add the olive oil to the frying pan and sauté the falafel for 3-4 minutes on each side until crisp and golden. Drain on kitchen paper.

To make the yoghurt dressing place the yoghurt in a bowl, stir in the cucumber and mint and season with black pepper.

Warm the pitta breads under a hot grill or in the toaster and split open, then stuff with the salad leaves, falafel and drizzle over the yoghurt dressing to serve.

typical nutritional content - *per portion*			
Energy Kcal (Calories)	495	Salt (g)	1.0
Fat (g)	15.1	Sugars (g)	5.8
of which saturates (g)	4.2		

healthy tips
fruit and vegetables – go for 5 a day!

Fruit and vegetables are virtually fat-free, packed with vitamins, minerals and fibre and are very important for the health of both adults and children. Aim to eat five servings of fruit and vegetables every day but remember to wash them before eating. Choose fruit and vegetables in a variety of colours to get the full range of nutrients. A high fruit and vegetable intake is associated with a reduced risk of developing heart disease and stroke.

Eating more fruit and vegetables

- Slice a banana over toast or an apple over cereal in the morning.
- Munch an apple while walking to school/work or waiting for the bus.
- Pack a mid-morning fruit snack.
- Liquidise fruit and add to yoghurts, milkshakes or smoothies.
- Fruit salads make a delicious dessert – or snack – or breakfast. Chop up whatever fruit you like – mix tinned fruit in natural juice and fresh fruit – it tastes sweet and delicious.
- Stock up on veg with your main meal (you can hide the veg in a child's meal by liquidising it).
- Overcooking vegetables destroys vitamins. Try steaming, microwaving or boiling vegetables in a little water with the saucepan lid on until tender.
- Keep washed fresh fruit or veg in the fridge in bite-sized pieces. They make great snacks for adults and children. Try carrots, tomatoes, apples, grapes, melon or anything that takes your fancy.

Swap it!

swap	for
Soft drink	Unsweetened fruit juice (no added sugar)
Fried chips	Baked potato or low-fat chips
Butter on baked potato	Chilli, herbs or low-fat yoghurt on baked potato
Mid-morning biscuit	Piece of fresh fruit or a smoothie
Extra meat and cheese in your sandwich	Lots of fresh salad such as cucumber, tomato, sweetcorn, peppers or beetroot

For more information visit **www.irishheart.ie** or read the Irish Heart Foundation's 'Good Eating' leaflet.

healthy tips
heart-healthy cooking

A healthy diet isn't simply determined by the foods we eat. The way these foods are prepared and cooked has a significant effect on their nutritional value. There are many healthy cooking methods available: boiling, baking, stir-frying, roasting, steaming, poaching and grilling.

Different cooking methods make an impact on calories

average potato portion	grams of fat	calories
Boiled (175g)	0.18g	126 kcal
Baked (180g)	0.36g	244 kcal
Mashed (3 scoops 180g, no butter, a little milk)	0.54g	120 kcal
Mashed (3 scoops 180g, with butter)	8.5g	187 kcal
Roast (200g, with blended oil)	9.0g	298 kcal
Chips (165g straight cut, in blended oil)	22.2g	450 kcal

Swap it!

swap	for
Adding extra oil to the frying pan	Adding a little extra water if the food starts to stick or using a spray oil to help control the amount used
Creamy sauces	Tomato-based sauces
Boiling vegetables until soft	Using a minimal amount of water, covering with a lid and cooking them until they are just tender
Salads with dressing	Dressings and sauces served on the side
Full-fat milk and cheese	Low-fat milk and cheese
Full-fat mayonnaise	Light mayonnaise or natural yogurt (e.g. in coleslaw and salad dressings)
Fried chips	Boil, steam, dry-roast or bake potatoes

For more information visit **www.irishheart.ie**.

Vegetables
& Salads

baked french potatoes

This dish is hassle-free, so is perfect for a dinner party or Sunday lunch. The potatoes take about the same time as a roast chicken and are just packed full of flavour. As they are quite moist there is no need for gravy.

Preparation time: 15 minutes • Cooking time: 1 hour 15 minutes • *Serves 6-8*

what you need

2 tablespoons olive oil
3 onions, thinly sliced
2 large garlic cloves, crushed
2 tablespoons fresh flat-leaf parsley, chopped

1.5kg (3lb) potatoes, peeled and thinly sliced
900ml (1½ pints) vegetable or chicken stock
freshly ground black pepper

what you do

Preheat the oven to 200°C/400°F/Gas Mark 6.

Heat half the oil in a frying pan and sauté the onions and garlic for 3-4 minutes until softened but not browned. Season lightly with pepper and stir in the parsley.

Layer the potatoes and onion mixture in a 1.75 litres (3 pint) baking dish, finishing with an attractive overlapping layer of the potatoes. Pour the stock over them – it should just cover the top of the potatoes. Season lightly with pepper. Drizzle the remaining tablespoon of olive oil on top.

Cover the dish tightly with tinfoil. Bake for 45 minutes, then remove the foil. Gently press the potatoes down. Bake for another 20-25 minutes until the top is crisp and golden brown.

Serve in its baking dish straight to the table.

typical nutritional content – *per portion*			
Energy Kcal (Calories)	176	Salt (g)	0.4
Fat (g)	3.3	Sugars (g)	2.4
of which saturates (g)	0.4		

baked mushrooms with garlic crumbs

These are fantastic served as a starter but they also make a delicious accompaniment to meat. Try to choose even-sized mushrooms with curled-up edges so that they hold the filling in place.

Preparation time: 5 minutes • Cooking time: 20 minutes • Serves 4

what you need

12 field mushrooms, each about 7.5cm (3in) in diameter
1 tablespoon olive oil, plus a little extra to oil the mushrooms
1 shallot, finely chopped
2 garlic cloves, finely chopped
50g (2oz) fresh soft brown breadcrumbs

2 tablespoons freshly grated Parmesan cheese
1 tablespoon fresh flat-leaf parsley, chopped
freshly ground black pepper

what you do

Preheat the oven to 180°C/350°F/Gas Mark 4.

Remove the stems from the mushrooms and, using your hand, lightly oil the outside of the cup of each mushroom to prevent them from sticking to the tin and drying out whilst cooking. Arrange the mushrooms, oiled side down, in a small non-stick roasting tin.

Heat the tablespoon of oil in a frying-pan and sauté the shallot for 2-3 minutes until softened but not browned. Stir in the garlic and sauté for another 30 seconds or so. Remove from the heat and season lightly with pepper. Stir in the breadcrumbs, Parmesan and parsley.

Add a heaped tablespoon of the mixture to each mushroom and then bake for 12-15 minutes or until the mushrooms are just cooked through and the breadcrumb topping is nicely golden.

Arrange on warmed plates to serve.

typical nutritional content – *per portion*			
Energy Kcal (Calories)	101	Salt (g)	0.3
Fat (g)	4.6	Sugars (g)	0.9
of which saturates (g)	1.0		

mixed bean salad with balsamic dressing

Once you have grilled the peppers make sure you give them a chance to cool down completely in a bowl covered with clingfilm as this allows the skin to steam off naturally, making them much easier to peel. It also helps to catch all the delicious natural juices that can be used in the dressing.

Preparation time: 10 minutes • Cooking time: 35 minutes • *Serves 6*

what you need

For the salad
2 large red peppers
225g (8oz) broad beans or peas, podded
175g (6oz) tin sweetcorn, drained and rinsed
400g (14oz) tin black-eyed beans, drained and rinsed
400g (14oz) tin kidney beans, drained and rinsed
1 small red onion, finely chopped

1 bunch flat-leaf parsley, leaves removed and roughly chopped
2 tablespoons torn fresh basil

For the dressing
3 tablespoons extra-virgin olive oil
1 tablespoon balsamic vinegar
1 garlic clove, crushed (optional)
freshly ground black pepper

what you do

To make the dressing, place the extra-virgin olive oil in a small bowl and whisk in the balsamic vinegar and the garlic (if using). Season lightly with pepper.

To prepare the salad, preheat the grill. Arrange the red peppers on a grill rack and cook for 20-30 minutes until well charred and blistered, turning regularly. Transfer to a large bowl and cover with clingfilm. Leave the peppers to cool completely, then peel, placing a bowl underneath to catch all of the juices. Slice the flesh into 1cm (½in) dice, discarding the seeds and cores. Place with juices in a large bowl and set aside.

Bring a small pan of water to the boil, tip in the broad beans or peas and cook for 2 minutes, then drain. If using broad beans, split the skins to pop out the beans. Add to the red peppers along with the sweetcorn, black-eyed beans, kidney beans, red onion and herbs.

Drizzle the dressing over and gently fold in, then cover with clingfilm and set aside at room temperature for an hour, if time allows, before serving.

typical nutritional content – *per portion*			
Energy Kcal (Calories)	217	Salt (g)	0.6
Fat (g)	7.0	Sugars (g)	9.0
of which saturates (g)	1.1		

baked root vegetables in a parcel

Use any selection of root vegetables you fancy. They can be prepared well in advance, leaving nothing to do at the last minute. The oven temperature can be quite flexible so simply place the vegetables on the bottom shelf of your oven and adjust the cooking time depending on what roast you are cooking.

Preparation time: 10 minutes • Cooking time: 1 hour • *Serves 6-8*

what you need

900g (2lb) carrots, parsnips and turnips
2 shallots, finely chopped
2 garlic cloves, finely chopped

1 teaspoon fresh thyme leaves
2 tablespoons olive oil
freshly ground black pepper

what you do

Preheat the oven to 180°C/350°F/Gas Mark 4.

Peel the carrots, parsnips and turnips and then cut into even-sized sticks. Take a large double sheet of parchment paper and pile the root vegetables in the middle.

Scatter the shallots, garlic and thyme over the vegetables and mix in the olive oil, then drizzle three tablespoons of water over them. Season lightly with pepper.

Fold in the sides of the parcel to enclose the vegetables. Twist the edges to seal.

Place the parchment parcel on a baking tray and roast for 1 hour until the root vegetables are tender and slightly caramelised.

To serve, either carefully transfer the root vegetables into a large warmed dish, or place the parchment parcel on a plate and open at the table.

typical nutritional content – *per portion*			
Energy Kcal (Calories)	72	Salt (g)	0.1
Fat (g)	3.4	Sugars (g)	6.8
of which saturates (g)	0.5		

braised red cabbage

This is a perfect vegetable to make in advance as it will keep well in the fridge for a couple of days and may be reheated very successfully. It is delicious served with pork or chicken, or even on its own with a jacket potato and a dollop of low-fat natural yoghurt sprinkled with freshly snipped chives.

Preparation time: 15 minutes • Cooking time: 2 hours • Serves 6

what you need

1 red cabbage
¼ teaspoon ground cinnamon
¼ teaspoon ground cloves
2 red onions, thinly sliced
1 large Bramley cooking apple, peeled, cored and grated

300ml (½ pint) cranberry juice
4 tablespoons red wine vinegar
2 tablespoons redcurrant jelly
freshly ground black pepper

what you do

Preheat the oven to 150°C/300°F/Gas Mark 2.

Trim the red cabbage and then cut into quarters. Cut out the tough stalks and then finely shred the remainder – you'll need 900g (2lb) in total. Arrange a layer of the shredded cabbage in the bottom of a large casserole dish that has a lid and add a little of the cinnamon and cloves along with a good grinding of black pepper.

Scatter a layer of the onions over the seasoned cabbage, followed by a layer of the apples, then sprinkle a little more of the spices on top. Continue layering in this way until all the ingredients have been used up, finishing with a layer of the cabbage.

Place the cranberry juice, vinegar and redcurrant jelly in a pan and simmer gently until the redcurrant jelly has dissolved, then pour over the layered cabbage. Cover tightly with tinfoil and the lid and bake for 2 hours until the cabbage is tender.

Transfer to a warmed dish and serve at once.

typical nutritional content – *per portion*			
Energy Kcal (Calories)	99	Salt (g)	0.2
Fat (g)	0.4	Sugars (g)	14.2
of which saturates (g)	0.0		

the perfect salad

It is crucial that every cook has a good salad up their sleeve. It can be served as a starter or instead of vegetables with your main course. This recipe gives you lots of ideas to help you to make your perfect salad!

Preparation time: 10 minutes · Cooking time: none · *Serves 4*

what you need

For the salad
1 oakleaf lettuce
2 Little Gem lettuces
4 spring onions, thinly sliced on the diagonal
1 bunch radishes, trimmed and thinly sliced
100g (4oz) semi-dried tomatoes, roughly chopped
2 tablespoons mixed toasted seeds

For the dressing
1 tablespoon fresh lemon juice
1 small garlic clove, crushed (optional)
1½ tablespoons olive oil
1 tablespoon rapeseed oil
freshly ground black pepper

what you do

To make the dressing, whisk the lemon juice with a little pepper in a bowl. Add the garlic (if using), and then whisk in the olive oil and rapeseed oil until they are well mixed.

Discard any outer damaged lettuce leaves and wash – a salad-spinner is handy for gently drying the leaves. Break the lettuce leaves into a salad bowl and scatter the spring onions, radishes, semi-dried tomatoes and mixed toasted seeds on top. Drizzle the dressing over the salad and toss until everything is lightly coated.

Serve immediately straight to the table.

variations

This recipe can be tailored to suit your own tastes and that of your guests so feel free to amend it accordingly, but try to choose a soft lettuce, a crunchy lettuce, a herb or some form of onion, a couple of vegetables and a crunchy topping. If you want to make your salad a more substantial meal, then add some cheese, for example, Parmesan shavings, crumbled feta cheese, goats' cheese or roughly torn Buffalo mozzarella – they are all delicious options.

Soft lettuce
Butterhead, baby spinach, lamb's or watercress

Crunchy lettuce
Cos, Frisby, chicory or radicchio

Herb or mild onion

Basil, mint, flat-leaf parsley, chives, rocket or shallots

Vegetable

Cucumber, tomatoes, carrots, celery or peppers

Optional extra

Orange or pink grapefruit segments, diced dessert apple, cooked baby beetroots or an avocado

Crunchy topping

Toasted pine nuts or walnuts, pumpkin seeds or rustic croutons (for home-made croutons toss small pieces of diced bread in a little olive oil and toast in a frying pan)

typical nutritional content – *per portion*			
Energy Kcal (Calories)	255	Salt (g)	0.6
Fat (g)	24.3	Sugars (g)	3.5
of which saturates (g)	3.0		

tuscan style green beans

These would also be delicious with two seeded and diced vine tomatoes added to the pan with the beans, particularly in summer when tomatoes are at their best.

Preparation time: 5 minutes • Cooking time: 10 minutes • *Serves 4*

what you need

450g (1lb) French or dwarf green beans, tails removed
1 tablespoon extra-virgin olive oil
1 garlic clove, crushed

2 tablespoons fresh flat-leaf parsley, chopped
2 tablespoons freshly grated Parmesan cheese
freshly ground black pepper

what you do

Plunge the French beans into a large pan of boiling water. Boil for 2 minutes until just tender. Drain and refresh under cold running water.

Return the pan to the heat with the olive oil. Tip in the garlic and then sauté for 20 seconds or so until sizzling but not browned. Add the beans and continue to sauté for a minute or two, then season lightly with pepper and fold in the parsley.

Tip into a warmed dish and scatter the Parmesan over to serve.

typical nutritional content – *per portion*			
Energy Kcal (Calories)	75	Salt (g)	0.1
Fat (g)	4.9	Sugars (g)	2.8
of which saturates (g)	1.5		

low fat chips

These chips are much healthier than regular deep-fried chips. They are perfect for a party or barbecue as they are baked in roasting tins in the oven and there is very little looking after to do. They're always a winner.

Preparation time: 5 minutes ◦ Cooking time: 45 minutes ◦ *Serves 4*

what you need

675g (1½lb) large potatoes
2 tablespoons sunflower oil
good pinch of paprika

what you do

Preheat the oven to 200°C/400°F/Gas Mark 6.

Scrub the potatoes and, keeping the skins on, cut each one into 6-8 even-sized wedges, depending on their size. Place the potatoes in a pan of boiling water, return to the boil and continue to boil for 2-3 minutes, then drain.

Put the sunflower oil in a large bowl and add the paprika, stirring to combine. Add the wedges and toss until well coated, then arrange them in rows sitting upright on their skins in two roasting tins. Bake for 25-30 minutes until completely tender and golden brown, swapping the roasting tins halfway through so all the chips cook evenly.

Tip onto a large warmed platter to serve.

typical nutritional content – *per portion*			
Energy Kcal (Calories)	176	Salt (g)	0.03
Fat (g)	5.8	Sugars (g)	1.0
of which saturates (g)	0.7		

triple rice salad with mango

This salad uses some Camargue rice which is now more readily available in supermarkets as well as in health food shops. It is a short-grained and unmilled variety of rice and is therefore quite sticky. It has an intense, somewhat nutty taste and a naturally chewy texture. As it is higher in fibre than white rice it is much more filling. You could always just use mixed long grain and wild rice instead. This salad would be delicious served with roast chicken or would be perfect for a picnic as it transports very well.

Preparation time: 15 minutes • Cooking time: 1 hour • *Serves 6-8*

what you need

For the rice salad
200g (7oz) mixed long and wild rice
200g (7oz) Camargue red rice
2 tablespoons fresh mint, roughly
chopped
2 tablespoons fresh coriander, roughly
chopped
2 spring onions, thinly sliced
1 large firm ripe mango
1 red pepper, seeded and very
thinly sliced
50g (2oz) unsalted roasted peanuts

50g (2oz) coconut shavings or
coconut chips (optional)

For the dressing
juice of 2 limes
1 small lemongrass stalk, chopped,
outer stalk removed
1 tablespoon maple syrup
½ teaspoon soy sauce
pinch of dried chilli flakes
1 tablespoon sesame oil
2 tablespoons sunflower oil

what you do

To make the dressing, place the lime juice in a small pan with the lemongrass, maple syrup, soy sauce and chilli flakes. Bring to a gentle simmer and then cook for 3-4 minutes until thick and syrupy. Remove from the heat and leave to cool, then strain into a bowl and whisk in the sesame oil and sunflower oil.

To prepare the rice salad, cook each type of rice in a separate pan of boiling water as instructed on the packet until just tender. Drain and place together in a large bowl. Stir in the herbs and spring onions with the dressing until evenly combined.

Peel the mango and cut the flesh into 2cm (¾in) dice, discarding the stone. Fold into the salad with the red pepper, peanuts and the coconut (if using). If time allows, cover with clingfilm and allow to sit at room temperature for up to 2 hours to allow the flavours to develop.

Give the salad a good stir before serving straight to the table.

typical nutritional content – *per portion*			
Energy Kcal (Calories)	318	Salt (g)	0.08
Fat (g)	11.8	Sugars (g)	6.5
of which saturates (g)	4.5		

soused coleslaw

Soused coleslaw is a lower-fat alternative to traditional coleslaw which is dressed with mayonnaise. In this recipe a reduced-fat French dressing is heated and added to the shredded vegetables. The result is a tasty and unusual salad that keeps well in the fridge for up to one week.

Preparation time: 10 minutes • Cooking time: none • *Serves 10-12*

what you need

For the coleslaw
½ head white cabbage, shredded, thick cores removed
4 carrots, grated
4 celery sticks, thinly sliced
1 onion, finely chopped

For the dressing
25g (1oz) caster sugar
50ml (2fl oz) sunflower oil
50ml (2fl oz) white wine vinegar
½ teaspoon Dijon mustard
1 teaspoon celery seeds (optional)
freshly ground black pepper

what you do

Place the cabbage in a large bowl with the carrots, celery and onion.

To make the dressing, place the sugar in a small pan with the sunflower oil, vinegar, mustard and celery seeds (if using). Bring to the boil and then immediately pour over the vegetables, tossing lightly to combine.

Cover the soused coleslaw with clingfilm and chill until needed.

Just before serving, remove the clingfilm, give the coleslaw a good stir and season with pepper. Serve straight to the table in its bowl.

typical nutritional content – *per portion*			
Energy Kcal (Calories)	65	Salt (g)	0.1
Fat (g)	4.4	Sugars (g)	5.5
of which saturates (g)	0.6		

healthy tips
are you ready to lose weight?

Are you ready to lose weight? Being overweight means that your heart has to work harder to pump blood around your body. Many people who are overweight for a long time develop high blood pressure or diabetes, which are both risk factors for heart disease and stroke.

Act now Being overweight or very overweight (obese) is mainly the result of too many calories in our diet and too little activity. So, if you are overweight, taking action now will help prevent you from becoming obese.

Getting the right balance Energy in (as food) and energy out (as activity) need to be balanced for a healthy weight. The Food Pyramid *(see page 230)* is a guide for food choices and to lose weight it is also important to include 60-75 minutes of moderate-intensity physical activity, such as walking, on most days of the week.

Weight loss for life Forget about dieting. Instead, follow a weight loss plan for life. Make small gradual changes to the food you eat and get more active. Even losing a small amount of weight has health benefits.

Tips for losing weight successfully
- Look carefully at the size of your food portions, especially when eating out.
- Follow the Food Pyramid guidelines *(see page 230)*.
- Focus on what you can eat rather than on what you can't.
- Be strict and limit your food choices from the top shelf of the Food Pyramid.
- Learn to recognise hunger. Eat small portions if you are not really hungry at mealtimes.

Swap it!

swap	for
Shopping on an empty stomach without a list	Shopping after a meal with a list
Large dinner plate	Smaller plate and fill it mostly with vegetables
Starter and a main meal	2 starter portions – this can help you feel more satisfied as you're not missing out on a course
Creamy high-fat dessert	Fruit-based dessert
Skipping breakfast	Having 3 meals a day – people who eat breakfast regularly are more likely to keep their weight down

For more information visit **www.irishheart.ie** or see the Irish Heart Foundation's leaflet 'Are you Ready to Lose Weight?'.

healthy tips
sugary sweet

Sugary foods don't satisfy the appetite as well as other foods. They are high in calories but provide minimal amounts of vitamins, minerals and fibre. Sugary foods are linked to excess weight, Type 2 diabetes and tooth decay.

Beware of sugar

- Eat less table sugar, jam, honey, biscuits, confectionery and sugary drinks.

- If you choose to eat a sugary food or have a sugary drink, do so with a meal as it will be less likely to cause tooth decay.

- Try to choose nutritious snacks such as fruit or yoghurt rather than sugary options.

Swap it!

swap	for
Sweets	A punnet of berries or other fruit
Chocolate	Popcorn, unsalted nuts, apples, banana
Biscuits	Fruit, yoghurt, smoothie
Soft drinks	Water, unsweetened fruit juice, milk or diet drinks

For more information visit **www.irishheart.ie** or read the Irish Heart Foundation's 'Good Eating' leaflet.

Desserts

apple crumble

This crumble freezes extremely well. Simply wrap the dish with freezer clingfilm or freeze the fruit and crumble mixture in separate freezer bags if you don't have spare baking dishes. To cook from frozen, cover with tinfoil and bake at 180°C/350°F/Gas Mark 4 for 90 minutes, removing the tinfoil for the last 15 minutes.

Preparation time: 10 mins • Cooking time: 45 mins + 5 mins cooling • *Serves 6-8*

what you need

For the filling
900g (2lb) Bramley apples, peeled, cored and sliced
150ml (¼ pint) unsweetened apple juice
2 tablespoons caster sugar

For the topping
100g (4oz) wholemeal flour

75g (3oz) butter
100g (4oz) muesli (with no added salt or sugar)
2 tablespoons light brown sugar (reduce sugar if fruit is sweet)

Greek-style yoghurt, to serve

what you do

Preheat the oven to 190°C/375°F/Gas Mark 5.

Place the apples in a 1.5 litre (2½ pint) ovenproof dish and pour the apple juice over them, then sprinkle the caster sugar on top.

To make the topping, tip the flour into a large bowl. Add the butter and rub in with your fingertips until the mixture resembles fine breadcrumbs. Stir in the muesli and brown sugar and scatter over the apple mixture to cover it completely. Bake for about 45 minutes until the topping is golden and crunchy.

Leave to cool for about 5 minutes and then divide between bowls and add a dollop of Greek yoghurt to each one to serve.

typical nutritional content – *per portion*			
Energy Kcal (Calories)	301	Salt (g)	0.3
Fat (g)	13.5	Sugars (g)	26.3
of which saturates (g)	8.2		

variations

Rhubarb and strawberry
Use 675g (1½lb) of chopped rhubarb with 225g (8oz) of hulled strawberries instead of the apple filling.

Raspberry and almond
Use 900g (2lb) of frozen raspberries for the filling and add 50g (2oz) of ground almonds to the topping.

one crust rhubarb pie

★ *RECIPE BY* Miriam O'Callaghan *Radio and Television Presenter*

This must be the perfect pie. It looks very attractive because it has only one layer of pastry and you can see the fruit inside! The recipe would also work well with gooseberries, raspberries or slices of Bramley apples, depending on what's in season.

Preparation time: 15 mins + 30 mins chilling • Cooking time: 40 mins • *Serves 4-6*

what you need

For the shortcrust pastry
100g (4oz) plain flour, plus a little
extra for dusting
50g (2oz) wholemeal flour
75g (3oz) polyunsaturated margarine,
at room temperature, plus a little extra
for greasing

For the filling
900g (2lb) bunch rhubarb
50g (2oz) caster sugar

For the glaze
1 small egg white
1 tablespoon caster sugar

Greek-style yoghurt, to serve

what you do

To make the pastry, sieve the plain and wholemeal flour into a bowl and then tip
in any wheat that is left in the bottom of the sieve. Using a fork or your fingers,
gently rub in the margarine. When the mixture reaches the crumb stage, sprinkle
in enough cold water to bring it together in a smooth dough that leaves the bowl
clean – you'll need only a couple of tablespoons in total. Give it a little light knead
on a lightly floured board to bring it fully together, then place the pastry in a
polythene bag in the fridge for 30 minutes.

Preheat the oven to 200°C/400°F/Gas Mark 6.

Trim down the stalks of rhubarb and cut it into 2.5cm (1in) pieces – you'll need
675g (1½lb) in total. Lightly flour the work surface and roll the pastry to a round
of approximately 25cm (10in). As you roll, give it quarter-turns so that it ends up
as round as you can make it. Now carefully roll the pastry around the rolling pin
and transfer it to the centre of a lightly greased baking sheet. Pile the prepared
fruit in the centre of the pastry, sprinkling the caster sugar as you go. Then turn
the edges of the pastry up and inwards to make a case to hold in the fruit; if any
breaks, patch it back on again – it's meant to be rough and ragged!

For the glaze, brush the surface of the pastry with the egg white and sprinkle
the caster sugar over it. Bake for 35 minutes or until the crust is golden brown
and the rhubarb is tender but still holding its shape.

Serve straight to the table with a bowl of Greek-style yoghurt.

typical nutritional content – *per portion*			
Energy Kcal (Calories)	247	Salt (g)	0.3
Fat (g)	12.2	Sugars (g)	13.3
of which saturates (g)	3.1		

passion fruit zabaglione with fresh berries

★ RECIPE BY Piero Melis THE COURTHOUSE RESTAURANT Kinlough, Co Leitrim

This zabaglione, a classic Italian dessert, may also be used as a sauce on frozen yoghurt. If you have Marsala wine from your travels you could also try Marty Whelan's Veal Marsala.

Preparation time: 15 minutes • Cooking time: 15 minutes • Serves 6

what you need

5 egg yolks
150g (5oz) caster sugar
120ml (4fl oz) sweet white wine or
Marsala
5 tablespoons passion fruit pulp

150g (5oz) blueberries
150g (5oz) raspberries
150g (5oz) small strawberries, hulled
and halved

what you do

Place the egg yolks and sugar in a large heatproof bowl and beat together until pale and fluffy, then beat in the sweet wine or Marsala, a little at a time.

Place the bowl over a pan of barely simmering water and cook over a low heat for about 15 minutes, whisking constantly, until the mixture starts to rise and is very thick and creamy. It is important not to allow the bowl to overheat. It will be ready when it forms soft mounds. Remove the bowl from the heat and continue beating for a further 5 minutes. Fold in the passion fruit pulp.

Arrange the berries in pretty glasses set on plates and spoon the passion fruit zabaglione on top to serve.

typical nutritional content – *per portion*			
Energy Kcal (Calories)	191	Salt (g)	0.04
Fat (g)	4.8	Sugars (g)	32.0
of which saturates (g)	1.3		

baked bramley apples

There are numerous variations when it comes to stuffing Bramley apples. For a change, substitute raisins, sultanas or even dates for the apricots, or try a mixture. Sweet mincemeat also works a treat at Christmas time.

Preparation time: 10 minutes • Cooking time: 50 minutes • Serves 4

what you need

4 x 225g (8oz) Bramley cooking apples
50g (2oz) ready-to-eat apricots, finely diced
4 heaped tablespoons runny honey
40g (1½oz) toasted flaked almonds

4 teaspoons softened butter, plus a little extra

vanilla frozen yoghurt, to serve

what you do

Preheat the oven to 180°C/350°F/Gas Mark 4.

Remove the centre core from each apple and then run the tip of a sharp knife around the circumference of each one, just piercing the skin – this helps stop them bursting whilst cooking. Arrange the apples in a lightly greased ovenproof dish that is approximately 23cm (9in square).

Place the apricots in a bowl with the honey and almonds and stir to combine, then divide between the cavities of the apples and pile up the excess in a dome on top of each fruit. Top each one with a teaspoon of butter and bake for about 45 minutes, basting with the juice every 10-15 minutes until the apples are completely tender but still holding their shape. Cover the tops of the apples with small pieces of tinfoil if they start to brown too quickly.

Transfer the apples to wide-rimmed bowls and drizzle the juices from the ovenproof dish over them. Serve hot with a scoop of vanilla frozen yoghurt.

typical nutritional content – per portion			
Energy Kcal (Calories)	319	Salt (g)	0.2
Fat (g)	14.6	Sugars (g)	43.5
of which saturates (g)	5.8		

blueberry and lemon cheesecake

This cheesecake is extremely easy because it does not require any gelatine. The action of the lemon juice on the cream cheese and crème fraîche helps it to set all on its own.

Preparation time: 15 mins + 2 hrs chilling • Cooking time: 5 mins • *Serves 8-10*

what you need

For the base
50g (2oz) butter
225g (8oz) light digestive biscuits

For the filling
200g (7oz) carton light cream cheese, or 200g Quark (skimmed-milk soft cheese) for a lower-fat option

50g (2oz) caster sugar
finely grated rind and juice of 1 lemon
200g (7oz) carton half-fat crème fraîche

For the topping
225g (8oz) blueberries

what you do

For the base, put the butter into a large pan and melt over a low heat. Put the digestive biscuits into a plastic bag, seal the end and crush with a rolling pin into fine crumbs. Stir the biscuit crumbs into the butter, then, using the back of a spoon, press the mixture firmly into the base and sides of a 25cm (10in) loose-bottomed flan tin that is about 2.5cm (1in) deep. Chill while you make the filling.

To make the filling, beat together the cream cheese (or Quark, if using), sugar and lemon rind in a bowl until smooth. Very gradually, beat in the lemon juice until you have a thick, creamy mixture, then gently fold in the crème fraîche. Spoon the filling onto the biscuit base, smooth the top with a knife and chill for at least 2 hours.

Remove the cheesecake from the flan tin and transfer it to a serving plate. Spoon the fresh blueberries over the top, then cut into wedges to serve.

typical nutritional content – *per portion*			
Energy Kcal (Calories)	225	Salt (g)	0.7
Fat (g)	13.3	Sugars (g)	10.8
of which saturates (g)	7.7		

apple and blackberry filo parcels

These apple and blackberry parcels look good and taste delicious. In early autumn why not spend a Saturday afternoon in the country picking fresh blackberries from the hedgerows and use them for a Sunday dessert? Frozen fruit will also work well and is just as good for you.

Preparation time: 10 minutes • Cooking time: 25 minutes • *Serves 4*

what you need

For the filling
15g (½oz) butter
4 dessert apples, peeled, cored and cut into slices
50g (2oz) caster sugar
good squeeze of lemon juice
225g (8oz) blackberries

For the pastry
40g (1½oz) unsalted butter
275g (10oz) packet frozen filo pastry, thawed
icing sugar, to dust

pouring custard made with low-fat milk or natural yoghurt, to serve

what you do

Pre-heat the oven to 200°C/400°F/Gas Mark 6.

To make the filling, heat a large heavy-based frying pan, add the butter and once it has melted toss in the apples and sprinkle half of the sugar over them, followed by the squeeze of lemon juice. Sauté for 3-4 minutes, tossing occasionally until lightly golden. Add the blackberries and continue to toss for another 30 seconds or so until just warmed through. Leave to cool.

Melt the unsalted butter in a small pan or in the microwave. Cut the filo pastry into 25cm (10in) squares and sprinkle the rest of the sugar over them, then layer up three squares, lightly brushing with melted butter between each layer and keeping the rest of the pastry covered with a damp tea towel whilst you work.

Spoon a quarter of the apple and blackberry mixture about 7.5cm (3in) away from one of the corners and roll the pastry over to enclose the filling completely, then fold in the two sides and roll up like a parcel. Brush lightly with melted butter and place on a non-stick baking sheet. Chill while you finish making the remaining three filo parcels.

Bake the apple and blackberry filo parcels for 12-15 minutes until the pastry is cooked through and golden brown.

Transfer each filo parcel to a warmed plate and add a light dusting of icing sugar. Add a couple of spoonfuls of custard to serve, if liked, or natural yoghurt.

typical nutritional content – *per portion*			
Energy Kcal (Calories)	443	Salt (g)	0.7
Fat (g)	13.9	Sugars (g)	30.4
of which saturates (g)	7.5		

lavender blancmange and strawberry coulis

★ *RECIPE BY* Ross Lewis CHAPTER ONE *Parnell Square, Dublin 1*

This dessert is perfect for entertaining as the blancmange can be made up to two days in advance. If you have difficulty removing the blancmanges from the moulds, dip the moulds briefly into hot water, without allowing the water to get into the blancmange, and then gently pull the pudding away from the sides with a small palette knife. Dried lavender is available in most large supermarkets or delis, or of course you can always dry your own from the garden.

Preparation time: 15 mins + 4 hrs chilling • **Cooking time:** 15 mins • *Serves 4*

what you need

For the blancmange
500ml (18fl oz) low-fat milk
1 vanilla pod, split open
1 tablespoon dried lavender
4 tablespoons caster sugar
2 gelatine leaves

For the strawberry coulis
350g (12oz) strawberries, hulled and
roughly chopped, plus 4 extra to
decorate
1 tablespoon caster sugar
1 tablespoon Grand Marnier
(orange liqueur)

what you do

To make the blancmange, place the milk in a heavy-based pan with the vanilla pod and lavender and gently bring to the boil. When it starts to creep up the sides of the pan, adjust the heat so that it maintains a medium boil and cook for a few minutes to allow the flavours to combine.

Meanwhile, place the gelatine leaves in a bowl of cold water to soak for 10 minutes until they soften.

Stir the sugar into the infused milk and allow to dissolve. Remove from the heat and leave to cool a little. Drain the gelatine leaves and gently squeeze dry. Add to the pan and whisk continuously until dissolved. Leave to cool.

Pass the mixture through a fine sieve and then divide equally among four 120ml (4fl oz) moulds or ramekins. Place on a baking sheet and leave to set in the fridge for at least 4 hours or overnight if possible.

To make the strawberry coulis, place the strawberries in a pan with the sugar and Grand Marnier and simmer gently for 4-5 minutes, then blend in a food processor and pass through a sieve into a bowl. Cover and chill until needed.

Turn the moulds or ramekins upside down onto plates and drizzle the strawberry coulis around the blancmange. Cut the four remaining strawberries in half and use to decorate the plates to serve.

typical nutritional content – *per portion*			
Energy Kcal (Calories)	197	Salt (g)	0.2
Fat (g)	2.1	Sugars (g)	39.7
of which saturates (g)	1.3		

exotic fruit pavlova

This is an all-time family favourite and you can vary it by choosing fruit depending on the season and what is available in the shops. For the perfect Pavlova leave the meringue in the turned-off oven with the door shut – this guarantees that the middle will develop the characteristic Pavlova marshmallowiness. The meringue can be prepared the day before and kept in a cool place until needed.

Preparation time: 15 mins • **Cooking time:** 1 hr + 1 hr cooling • *Serves 4*

what you need

For the meringue
2 large egg whites, at room
temperature
a pinch of salt
100g (4oz) caster sugar
1 teaspoon cornflour
½ teaspoon white wine vinegar
2 drops vanilla extract

For the topping
5 tablespoons light cream
25g (1oz) caster sugar

100g (4oz) half-fat crème fraîche
1 passion fruit, halved and pulp
removed
1 kiwi fruit, peeled and sliced
1 small orange, segmented
1 small star fruit, sliced
4 large strawberries
100g (4oz) raspberries

fresh mint sprigs, to garnish

what you do

Preheat the oven to 150°C/300°F/Gas Mark 2.

Line a baking tray with non-stick baking parchment and draw an 18cm (7in) circle on it.

To make the meringue, whisk the egg whites and salt in a large clean bowl until stiff peaks have formed. Whisk in the sugar, a third at a time, whisking well after each addition until stiff and very shiny. Sprinkle in the cornflour, vinegar and vanilla extract and gently fold in with a metal spoon.

Pile the meringue onto the baking parchment within the circle, making sure there is a substantial hollow in the centre.

Place in the oven and immediately reduce the heat to 110°C/225°F/Gas Mark ¼ and continue to cook for 45 minutes to 1 hour until crisp but still a little soft in the centre. Turn off the oven and leave to cool completely, with the door shut.

To make the filling, place the light cream in a bowl with the caster sugar and whip until thickened, then fold in the crème fraîche.

Peel the parchment off the meringue and transfer it to a serving plate. Pile the cream mixture into the hollow in the meringue and arrange all of the prepared fruit and berries on top, finishing with the passion fruit pulp.

Decorate with the mint sprigs, then cut into wedges to serve.

typical nutritional content – *per portion*			
Energy Kcal (Calories)	238	Salt (g)	0.1
Fat (g)	7.5	Sugars (g)	39.7
of which saturates (g)	4.8		

fresh fruit platter

Feel free to leave the skin on the pieces of fruit for this dessert, so that there is something to hold on to when dipping them in the passion fruit cream. Alternatively, serve with cocktail sticks or dessert forks. Experiment with the wide selection of different tropical fruits now readily available.

Preparation time: 20 minutes • **Cooking time:** none • *Serves 6*

what you need

For the passion fruit cream
4 passion fruit
200g (7oz) carton half-fat crème fraîche
finely grated rind of ½ small orange
2 tablespoons freshly squeezed orange juice
1 tablespoon icing sugar, sifted

For the fruit platter
2 ripe nectarines or peaches

2 red-skinned apples
1 bunch of green or red grapes
4 ripe figs
1 ripe small melon (such as Galia)
1 star fruit
100g (4oz) strawberries
1 small pomegranate

plenty of crushed ice, to serve (optional) – place ice-cubes in a plastic bag and crush with a rolling pin

what you do

For the passion fruit cream, cut the passion fruit in half and scoop out the pulp into a bowl. Beat the crème fraîche with a spoon until smooth and fluffy, then fold in the orange rind and juice with the passion fruit pulp and icing sugar so that the mixture remains softly whipped. Spoon the mixture into a small serving bowl, cover with clingfilm and set aside to chill and firm up in the fridge.

Cut the fruit into one-portion pieces, discarding any seeds and stones. The pomegranate needs to be cut in half and the seeds removed, discarding the yellow pith. Place the prepared fruit on a tray, cover with clingfilm and chill in the fridge until just before you are ready to serve.

Cover a large, round plate or tray with lots of crushed ice, if using, and nestle a bowl of passion fruit cream in the centre. Arrange the chilled prepared fruits attractively and serve immediately.

typical nutritional content – *per portion*			
Energy Kcal (Calories)	229	Salt (g)	0.2
Fat (g)	5.9	Sugars (g)	42.0
of which saturates (g)	3.4		

grilled nectarines with pistachio brittle

This dessert is packed full of different textures, all of which you get in one mouthful! The sweet, sticky nectarines with cool, creamy yoghurt and crisp nutty brittle is a delicious combination. This indulgent pudding is sure to delight all of your guests.

Preparation time: 10 minutes • Cooking time: 15 minutes • *Serves 4*

what you need

75g (3oz) caster sugar
25g (1oz) shelled unsalted pistachio nuts, roughly chopped
4 ripe large nectarines or peaches

1 tablespoon apricot conserve (or apricot jam)
4 heaped tablespoons Greek-style yoghurt

what you do

Preheat the grill to high. Line a sturdy baking tin with non-stick parchment paper. Sprinkle the sugar into the base of a heavy-based pan and scatter the pistachio nuts on top. Heat gently for 2-3 minutes until the mixture is a golden colour, being very careful not to overcook. Immediately pour the mixture onto the lined baking tin and leave to cool and harden. It is essential that you do this quickly to prevent the sugar from turning black, which can happen in seconds.

Meanwhile, cut each nectarine or peach in half and remove the stones. Arrange them cut-side up in an ovenproof dish and brush lightly with the apricot conserve or jam. Pop under the grill for 8-10 minutes until sticky and golden, basting occasionally with the juices of the fruit.

Transfer the nectarines onto plates and add a dollop of yoghurt to each one. Roughly break up the pistachio brittle and scatter on top to serve.

typical nutritional content – *per portion*			
Energy Kcal (Calories)	215	Salt (g)	0.1
Fat (g)	6.6	Sugars (g)	36.1
of which saturates (g)	3.3		

mango and lime granita

This granita is halfway between a drink and a sorbet – the mixture is so refreshing and the texture is icy enough to eat with a teaspoon. It looks like sequins sparkling in a glass and is lovely to serve after a spicy meal as a palate refresher. This recipe can also be made in an ice-cream machine; simply follow the manufacturer's instructions.

Preparation time: 3 hours • Cooking time: none • Serves 4-6

what you need

2 large ripe mangoes
50g (2oz) caster sugar
juice of 4 limes
600ml (1 pint) soda water or sparkling water

what you do

Peel the mangoes and then cut the flesh into a food processor, discarding the stones. Add the sugar and lime juice. Blend to a purée and then add the soda or sparkling water and blend again until smooth.

Transfer the mixture to a large plastic container and freeze for 2 hours until partially frozen.

Remove the partially frozen granita from the freezer and beat with a fork to break down all of the ice crystals, then return to the freezer.

Continue to freeze the granita for another hour or so, removing from the freezer every 20 minutes to beat gently and break down the ice crystals. The longer you leave it in the freezer the more icy the texture will become.

If you plan to make this more than a few hours ahead, transfer to the fridge for 30 minutes before you are ready to serve and then break up the crystals with a fork. Spoon the granita into glasses and arrange them on plates with long-stemmed spoons to serve.

typical nutritional content – *per portion*			
Energy Kcal (Calories)	62	Salt (g)	0.01
Fat (g)	0.1	Sugars (g)	15.8
of which saturates (g)	0.0		

meringues with raspberries and vanilla cream

These meringues have a crisp exterior and delicious, marshmallow-like centres. They will keep for at least one week in an airtight container. Add the raspberries and vanilla cream topping just before serving or the meringues will go soft.

Preparation time: 15 mins • **Cooking time:** 50 mins + 3 hrs cooling • *Serves 6*

what you need

For the meringues
3 egg whites
pinch of salt
175g (6oz) caster sugar
1 teaspoon cornflour
½ teaspoon white wine vinegar

For the topping
1 vanilla pod
¼ teaspoon finely grated orange rind
200g (7oz) carton half-fat crème fraîche
225g (8oz) raspberries
½ teaspoon icing sugar

what you do

Preheat the oven to 140°C/275°F/Gas Mark 1.

Place the egg whites into a large bowl with the salt and whisk with a hand-held electric mixer until they form stiff peaks. Whisk in the sugar, a tablespoon at a time, to make a stiff glossy meringue. Whisk in the cornflour and vinegar.

Drop 6 even-sized spoonfuls of the meringue mixture onto a baking sheet lined with non-stick parchment paper, spacing them well apart, and flatten slightly with the back of a spoon, making a small dip in the centre. Bake for 45 minutes, then turn off the oven and leave them inside for 2-3 hours to go completely cold. This should stop them from cracking.

Just before serving, split the vanilla pod and scrape the seeds out, then stir the vanilla seeds and orange rind into the crème fraîche. Spoon a small dollop of the vanilla cream onto the centre of each plate and sit the meringues on top to prevent them from sliding around on the plates, then fill with the rest of the vanilla cream.

Pile the raspberries on top and add a light dusting of icing sugar to serve.

typical nutritional content – *per portion*			
Energy Kcal (Calories)	183	Salt (g)	0.1
Fat (g)	5.1	Sugars (g)	32.7
of which saturates (g)	3.4		

red fruit terrine

This is a great dessert for a dinner party. It can be made well in advance, with very little to do at the last minute.

Preparation time: 30 mins + 3 hrs chilling • Cooking time: none • *Serves 6*

what you need

50g (2oz) caster sugar
250ml (9fl oz) orange Muscat or
Sauternes wine (sweet)
juice of 1 lemon
4 teaspoons powdered gelatine
225g (8oz) strawberries

200g (7oz) redcurrants
225g (8oz) raspberries
6 fresh mint or lemon geranium
leaves
6 tablespoons Greek-style yoghurt

what you do

For the syrup, place the sugar and 250ml (9fl oz) of water in a heavy-based pan. Dissolve over a low heat, bring to the boil and simmer for 1 minute. Pour into a bowl and leave to cool, then stir in the wine and lemon juice.

Sprinkle the gelatine over four tablespoons of water in a small heatproof bowl and leave to soak and swell for 2-3 minutes. Set the bowl over a pan of gently simmering water and leave for another 2-3 minutes until the gelatine has dissolved. Stir into the syrup and leave to cool.

Wash the redcurrants, strawberries and raspberries. Strip the redcurrants of their stalks. Hull and slice the strawberries. Place a 1.2 litre (2 pint) loaf tin in a roasting tin with ice cubes and cold water coming halfway up its sides. Place a layer of redcurrants in the loaf tin. Spoon enough of the liquid jelly over to cover the redcurrants and leave to set.

Layer the strawberries and raspberries in the tin, on top of the set jelly, with the mint or lemon geranium leaves. Carefully spoon the rest of the jelly mixture over to fill the tin. If you find the jelly has begun to set a little, warm the bowl over a pan of simmering water. Leave the loaf tin in the roasting tin until the jelly is just set. Transfer the loaf tin to the fridge and leave until set completely – at least 3 hours or preferably overnight.

Fill a large bowl with hot water. Dip the loaf tin in the water for 3-4 seconds. Immediately invert onto a flat platter, gently shaking the tin to release the jelly. Lift off the tin.

Slice and arrange on plates with a dollop of yoghurt to serve.

typical nutritional content – *per portion*			
Energy Kcal (Calories)	171	Salt (g)	0.1
Fat (g)	4.7	Sugars (g)	18.7
of which saturates (g)	3.1		

mocha chocolate mousse pots

These mousse pots are perfectly decadent with just a hint of coffee and cardamom – delicious! They are perfect for an indulgent treat or for a special occasion. The higher the percentage of cocoa in the chocolate you use, the better the mousse will taste. The minimum should be 50 per cent cocoa. A good dollop of crème fraîche or thick Greek-style yoghurt to serve will cut through the richness.

Preparation time: 1 hour • Cooking time: 5 minutes • *Serves 4*

what you need

150g (5oz) plain chocolate, broken into chunks (70% cocoa solids, if possible)
85ml (3fl oz) warm strong black coffee

2 cardamom pods, lightly crushed
2 eggs, separated
2 tablespoons caster sugar

half-fat crème fraîche or Greek-style yoghurt and mixed berries, to serve

what you do

Place four 120ml (4fl oz) ramekins or serving-glasses in the fridge; this will help the mousse pots to set quickly. Place the chocolate in a large heatproof bowl with the coffee and cardamom seeds. Set over a pan of simmering water for about 3 minutes until the chocolate has melted, stirring occasionally with a wooden spoon and making sure that the bowl is not touching the water. Remove from the heat and set aside to cool slightly.

Once the flavoured chocolate has cooled for a few minutes, remove the cardamom pods. Then beat in the egg yolks one at a time, using a wooden spoon. Place the egg whites in a separate bowl and using a balloon whisk or an electric beater, whisk until you have achieved soft peaks. Tip in the caster sugar and continue to beat until the mixture is glossy and meringue-like.

With a large metal spoon, gently stir a spoonful of the egg white into the melted flavoured chocolate; this should help loosen the chocolate. Fold in the rest of the egg white very gently in order to keep the air in. Spoon the mixture into the chilled ramekins or glasses and chill for at least 40 minutes (or up to 2 hours if time allows).

Arrange on plates and top each one with a good dollop of crème fraîche or yoghurt and scatter with a few berries to serve.

typical nutritional content – *per portion*			
Energy Kcal (Calories)	290	Salt (g)	0.1
Fat (g)	14.9	Sugars (g)	34.7
of which saturates (g)	8.2		

raspberry and hazelnut frozen yoghurt

This delicious dessert is really refreshing. If you would prefer a smoother mixture, blend the raspberries with the sugar in a food processor and then sieve the raspberry purée to remove the pips.

Preparation time: 10 mins + 4 hrs chilling • Cooking time: 10 mins • *Serves 8-10*

what you need

75g (3oz) hazelnuts
400g (14oz) frozen raspberries, thawed
50g (2oz) icing sugar

500g (1lb 2oz) low-fat natural yoghurt
fresh mint leaves, to decorate

what you do

Preheat the oven to 180°C/350°F/Gas Mark 4.

Place the hazelnuts in a small roasting tin and toast for about 5 minutes until golden brown. Remove and, once cool enough to handle, rub off the skins in a clean tea towel, then roughly chop the nuts.

Line a 1.2 litre (2 pint) non-stick loaf tin with freezer clingfilm. Place the raspberries in a bowl and sift the icing sugar over. Then gently mash using a potato-masher or fork. Fold in the yoghurt and toasted hazelnuts. Spoon into the prepared loaf tin, levelling off the surface. Cover with freezer clingfilm and freeze for at least 4 hours or overnight if possible.

To serve, turn the frozen yoghurt out of the tin onto a flat plate and, using a serrated or electric knife, cut into slices and arrange on plates. Decorate with the mint sprigs to serve.

typical nutritional content – *per portion*			
Energy Kcal (Calories)	107	Salt (g)	0.1
Fat (g)	5.4	Sugars (g)	10.9
of which saturates (g)	0.7		

scented roast plums with lime yoghurt

★ *RECIPE BY* Avoca Cafés *Kilmacanogue, Co Wicklow and 9 stores nationwide*

The lavender or rosemary gives the plums a wonderfully surprising scent. Choose sturdy stalks and if you are having difficulty piercing the plums without damaging the stalks try using a metal skewer to make a hole first.

Preparation time: 10 mins ● **Cooking time:** 25 mins ● *Serves 4*

what you need

For the scented plums
4 plums, halved and stoned
4 fresh lavender or rosemary stalks
25g (1oz) light brown sugar
1 teaspoon brandy
4 tablespoons clear honey

For the lime yoghurt
150g (5oz) low-fat natural yoghurt
finely grated rind of 2 limes
1 teaspoon icing sugar, sifted

what you do

Preheat the oven to 180°C/350°F/Gas Mark 4.

Carefully thread the plums onto lavender or rosemary stalks, then cover the ends of the stalks with tinfoil to prevent them from burning. Arrange in a small baking dish and sprinkle the brown sugar and brandy over. Roast for 15-20 minutes until the plums are just beginning to caramelise but are still holding their shape.

Meanwhile, make the lime yoghurt. Mix the yoghurt in a bowl with the lime rind and icing sugar. Cover with clingfilm and chill until needed.

When the plums are almost cooked, warm the honey in a small pan.

Transfer the scented roast plums onto plates. Remove the tinfoil and spoon the warm honey over. Add a dollop of the lime yoghurt to each one to serve.

typical nutritional content – *per portion*			
Energy Kcal (Calories)	142	Salt (g)	0.1
Fat (g)	0.5	Sugars (g)	33.7
of which saturates (g)	0.3		

rhubarb and orange fool

Adding orange rind to rhubarb gives it a really delicious flavour. For a quick, easy and tasty summer dessert, this one is hard to beat! It would also work very well with gooseberries and using a lime instead of the orange. The amount of sugar you use in this dessert will always depend on the natural sweetness of the fruit you are using.

Preparation time: 10 mins + 15 mins cooling • **Cooking time:** 20 mins • *Serves 4*

what you need

500g (1lb 2oz) bunch rhubarb, trimmed
and cut into 2.5cm (1in) pieces
finely grated rind and juice of 1 large orange
75g (3oz) caster sugar
500g (1lb 2oz) low-fat natural yoghurt

what you do

Preheat the oven to 200°C/400°F/Gas Mark 6.

Place the rhubarb, orange juice and rind in a shallow ovenproof dish and mix well to combine. Sprinkle the caster sugar over and bake for 15 minutes until the rhubarb is just tender but still holding its shape. Remove from the oven and leave to cool completely.

Tip the rhubarb mixture into a food processor and blend to a purée, then transfer to a bowl with a spatula and fold in the yoghurt. Divide among pretty glasses and chill for at least 2 hours or overnight if possible.

Serve straight from the fridge, set on plates.

typical nutritional content – *per portion*			
Energy Kcal (Calories)	157	Salt (g)	0.2
Fat (g)	1.4	Sugars (g)	30.6
of which saturates (g)	0.9		

summer fruit compote

This is a wonderful compote and you can use any selection of fresh fruit you fancy or dried fruits such as apricots, figs and prunes. Try it as a delicious breakfast treat at weekends. It will keep happily in the fridge for up to one week covered with clingfilm.

Preparation time: 10 mins • Cooking time: 10 mins + 15 mins cooling • *Serves 6-8*

what you need

2 large oranges
4 tablespoons caster sugar
1 vanilla pod
4 firm ripe peaches, peeled, halved,
stoned and cut into slices
3 firm ripe plums, halved, stoned and
cut into slices
3 firm ripe figs, cut into slices

low-fat natural yoghurt or half-fat
crème fraîche, to serve

what you do

Finely grate the rind from one of the oranges and place in a pan. Squeeze out the juice from the two oranges and place in a measuring jug, then pour in enough water to make up 450ml (¾ pint) of liquid.

Pour the orange juice mixture into the pan. Split the vanilla pod in half, scrape out the seeds and add them, along with the sugar, to the pan. Simmer gently for a couple of minutes until the sugar has dissolved, whisking until the vanilla is evenly distributed.

Add the peaches and plums to the orange juice mixture and then cover with a lid. Simmer gently for 3-4 minutes or until the fruit slices are softened but still holding their shape. Stir in the figs and then remove from the heat. Leave to cool for at least 15 minutes.

Spoon the compote into bowls and add a spoonful of natural yoghurt or half-fat crème fraîche to serve.

typical nutritional content – *per portion*			
Energy Kcal (Calories)	106	Salt (g)	0.1
Fat (g)	0.6	Sugars (g)	23.1
of which saturates (g)	0.3		

spiced poached pears with red wine and yoghurt

★ RECIPE BY BEAUFIELD MEWS *Woodlands Avenue, Stillorgan, Co Dublin*

This delightful dessert will revive even the most jaded palate. The pears improve with keeping, making this an excellent dessert for entertaining. Choose fruit that is perfectly ripe but still quite firm so that the flesh doesn't go mushy while you are preparing them.

Preparation time: 10 mins • Cooking time: 55 mins + 30 mins cooling • *Serves 4*

what you need

150ml (¼ pint) red wine
150ml (¼ pint) light cranberry juice
2 tablespoons honey
juice and finely grated rind of 1 lemon
juice and finely grated rind of 1 orange
1 cinnamon stick, broken in half

2 whole star anise
6 black peppercorns
2 whole cloves
4 firm ripe large pears
275g (10oz) low-fat natural yoghurt

what you do

Place the red wine in a deep-sided pan with a lid (it needs to be just large enough to hold the pears in an upright position). Add the cranberry juice, honey, lemon juice and rind and half of the orange juice and rind. Bring to the boil and then add the cinnamon stick, star anise, peppercorns and cloves. Reduce the heat and allow to simmer gently for another few minutes to allow the flavours to infuse. Peel the pears, leaving the stalks attached. Add the pears, standing them upright in the pan. Cover with the lid and simmer gently for 20-35 minutes until they are just tender, basting them from time to time with the liquid. The cooking time will depend on the ripeness of the pears.

Using a slotted spoon, transfer the pears to a dish and set aside. Boil the liquid in the pan until reduced in volume by half to a more syrupy consistency. Leave to cool.

Mix the remaining orange juice and rind into the yoghurt and divide among the serving dishes. Place a cooled poached pear on top of each one and then ladle the remaining cooking liquid over to serve.

typical nutritional content – *per portion*			
Energy Kcal (Calories)	109	Salt (g)	0.2
Fat (g)	0.6	Sugars (g)	11.0
of which saturates (g)	0.4		

mixed berry tiramisu

This is an excellent low-fat version of a much-loved dessert. It's really delicious and everyone will enjoy the sweet berry taste.

Preparation time: 40 minutes • Cooking time: none • Serves 4

what you need

25g (1oz) caster sugar
2 x 250g (9oz) cartons Quark
(skimmed-milk soft cheese) or 500g
(1lb 2oz) natural set yoghurt
3 tablespoons Kahlúa (coffee liqueur)
4 tablespoons strong black coffee
50g (2oz) sponge fingers, snapped in half

225g (8oz) mixed berries (such as
blueberries, raspberries and halved
strawberries)
25g (1oz) plain chocolate, finely
grated

what you do

Place the caster sugar in a large bowl with the Quark or yoghurt and then beat until really smooth.

Mix the coffee liqueur and coffee in a shallow bowl. Snap some of the sponge fingers into quarters and then dip in the coffee mixture. Arrange in the base of four Martini glasses or dessert glasses. Scatter half of the berries over and spoon half of the creamy mixture on top. Cover with half of the grated chocolate.

Repeat the layers all over again until all of the ingredients have been used up, finishing with a layer of the grated chocolate. Chill for at least 30 minutes.

Before serving, set the glasses on plates.

typical nutritional content – *per portion*			
Energy Kcal (Calories)	246	Salt (g)	0.3
Fat (g)	3.1	Sugars (g)	26.5
of which saturates (g)	1.6		

healthy tips
a heart-healthy home

A child's heart for life . . . some golden rules

High five for fruit and veg: Five portions of fruit and veg boost intakes of important vitamins for heart health.

Variety is the spice of life: Break old eating habits – gradually – and buy healthier options. The more foods children are exposed to, the more balanced their diet.

Turn off the TV more often: DVDs and computer games may be educational – at a stretch! – but children need 60 minutes of physical activity every day. And don't underestimate the power of TV in promoting sugary, high-fat and high-salt foods.

The 'S' words: Some processed foods contain lots of saturated fat, sugar and salt. Buy fresh foods wherever possible.

Role models: Children will put a value on healthy eating if that is the message they receive from their parents. Children copy what their parents do so it's important to lead by example.

Kids in the kitchen

Cooking and baking can be fun for you and your child. Enjoy experimenting with different dishes and engaging a child's five senses: seeing, touching, tasting, smelling – and hearing you laugh!

- It can be easy! If children are taught how to boil an egg, they'll be able to boil any kind of vegetable.
- Try the taste test. Line up fresh and processed produce. Get your child to close his or her eyes and taste the difference.
- Playing with ingredients is important, for example making something vaguely resembling scones. It's all about making children aware of what goes into food – and making a mess is part of the fun.

Swap it!

swap	for
Family members eating at different times	Family eating together around the table – young people who eat with their families consume fewer higher-calorie drinks, more fruit and vegetables, and less fat both at home and away from home
Offering processed foods	Offering fresh foods
Watching TV	Watching less TV and playing more games
Preparing your child's food	Involving your child in food preparation

For more information visit **www.irishheart.ie**.

healthy tips
alcohol – thinking about drinking

Small amounts of alcohol may provide some protection against heart disease, but there is not enough evidence to recommend including alcohol as part of a heart-healthy diet. Drinking large amounts of alcohol can increase blood pressure and may damage the liver and heart.

The recommended upper limits are:

Men   21 standard drinks a week
Women   14 standard drinks a week

1 standard drink (10 grams of alcohol)
= one half pint of beer, stout or lager
= one small glass of wine
= one pub measure of spirits (whiskey, vodka or gin)

Low risk drinking tips

- If you do drink, spread your drinking over the week.
- Keep some days alcohol-free.
- If you drink alcohol at home, try to use a measure.
- Remember that alcoholic drinks contain calories, for example two pints of beer have as many calories as a supersize chocolate bar.
- If you are watching your weight, try diet drinks, water or white wine spritzers.
- If you are pregnant or trying to conceive, you should avoid drinking alcohol.

Swap it!

swap	for
A glass of white wine	A white wine spritzer
Drinking on an empty stomach	Drinking with your meal
Some alcoholic drinks	Non-alcoholic drinks
Home measures of drinks	Accurate pub measures – for example, use a small wine glass (a bottle of wine has about eight standard drinks)

For more information visit www.irishheart.ie or read the Irish Heart Foundation's 'Good Eating' leaflet.

Breads
and Cakes

brown bread

★ RECIPE BY Honor Moore *Food Writer*

There are many different recipes for home-made brown bread, some using wholemeal flour alone, others mixing in plain white flour to lighten it, and others with different grains added. Made with the addition of a little butter, or a tablespoon of olive oil, the bread will keep fresh for a second day or can be frozen successfully.

Preparation time: 10 mins • Cooking time: 40 mins + 30 mins cooling • *Serves 6-8*

what you need

450g (1lb) wholemeal flour (coarse or medium), plus extra for dusting
175g (6oz) plain flour
1 teaspoon salt
1 teaspoon bread soda
15g (½oz) butter or 1 tablespoon

olive oil (optional)
1-2 teaspoons dark brown sugar (optional)
about 450ml (¾ pint) buttermilk, plus extra for brushing

what you do

Preheat the oven to 200°C/400°F/Gas Mark 6.

Put the wholemeal flour in a bowl. Sieve the plain flour, salt and bread soda together over the wholemeal flour and mix lightly. At this stage you may rub in the butter or stir in the oil and/or add the sugar, if desired. Make a well in the centre of the dry ingredients and pour in about two-thirds of the buttermilk. Mix, then gradually add just enough of the remaining buttermilk to give a soft dough.

Turn the dough out onto a clean surface dusted with wholemeal flour and knead lightly into a ball. Place on a sturdy non-stick baking tray and pat out into a round that is about 4cm (1½ins) thick. Brush with a little buttermilk and sprinkle lightly with wholemeal flour. Cut a cross into the bread and bake for 35-40 minutes, until the bread sounds hollow when tapped underneath.

Cool, wrapped in a tea towel, on a wire rack until ready to serve. Home-made brown bread is a delicious wholesome base for a tasty sandwich.

variations

White
Use all plain white flour to make white soda bread.

Cheese
Add 75g (3oz) of finely grated low-fat Cheddar instead of the sugar if using.

Herb
Add three tablespoons of chopped fresh mixed herbs, such as flat-leaf parsley, chives and basil instead of the sugar if using.

Mixed seeds

Add three tablespoons of mixed seeds to the dough or one tablespoon of mixed seeds on top.

Brown bread without olive oil and sugar

typical nutritional content – *per portion* *(basic recipe)*			
Energy Kcal (Calories)	270	Salt (g)	1.0
Fat (g)	1.8	Sugars (g)	4.3
of which saturates (g)	0.4		

With olive oil and sugar

typical nutritional content – *per portion*			
Energy Kcal (Calories)	280	Salt (g)	1.0
Fat (g)	3.1	Sugars (g)	4.8
of which saturates (g)	0.6		

banana cake

This delicious banana cake is great as a special treat. It is lower in fat than traditional banana cake because mashed-up bananas have been used to replace some of the oil. The more over-ripe your bananas are the better it tastes, so it is a great way of using up fruit that is past its best.

Preparation time: 15 mins • **Cooking time:** 15 mins + 20 mins cooling • *Serves 12*

what you need

For the cake
4 large ripe bananas
350g (12oz) self-raising flour
1 teaspoon bread soda
2 teaspoons mixed spice
175g (6oz) light brown sugar
3 large eggs
85ml (3fl oz) sunflower oil, plus extra for greasing

75g (3oz) sultanas
finely grated rind and juice of 1 orange
100g (4oz) walnuts, shelled and roughly chopped

For the filling
200g (7oz) light cream cheese
100g (4oz) icing sugar
finely grated rind of 1 orange

what you do

Preheat the oven to 180°C/350°F/Gas Mark 4.

Grease and line three 20cm (8in) sandwich tins with non-stick parchment paper. Peel the bananas and mash to a purée. Sieve the flour and bread soda into a large bowl. Mix in the spice and sugar. Blend in the eggs and the oil with a whisk until smooth.

Use a large fork to stir the mashed bananas, sultanas, orange rind, juice and walnuts into the flour. Stir well to combine.

Divide between the prepared tins. Bake for 15 minutes or until well risen and firm to the touch. A fine skewer through the middle of the cake should come out clean. Cool for 10 minutes, then remove from the tins. Peel off the parchment paper and leave to cool completely. This cake can be wrapped in tinfoil and keeps very well for up to 2 days.

Put the light cream cheese into a bowl and whisk until smooth. Gradually add the icing sugar to give a smooth filling. Stir in the orange rind. Cover with clingfilm and chill until needed.

When you are ready to serve the cake, spread a third of the filling over the top of each cake, then sandwich them all together, using the nicest one for the top.

Place on a cake stand and cut into slices to serve.

typical nutritional content – *per portion*			
Energy Kcal (Calories)	409	Salt (g)	0.7
Fat (g)	17.2	Sugars (g)	36.8
of which saturates (g)	3.7		

orange scented
bran muffins

The orange zest in this recipe is delicious! These muffins are simple to make and are best served on the day that they are made.

Preparation time: 10 mins + 10 mins standing • **Cooking time:** 25 mins + 5 mins cooling

Makes 10

what you need

50g (2oz) wheat bran
175ml (6fl oz) buttermilk
1 egg
4 tablespoons sunflower oil
50g (2oz) raisins
1 tablespoon treacle

finely grated rind of 1 orange
100g (4oz) plain flour
1 teaspoon bread soda
1 teaspoon ground cinnamon
100g (4oz) light brown sugar

what you do

Preheat the oven to 180°C/350°F/Gas Mark 4. Line a muffin tin with 10 deep paper cases.

Place the wheat bran in a large bowl with the buttermilk, egg, sunflower oil, raisins, treacle and orange rind. Allow to stand for 10 minutes to allow the flavour to develop.

Sieve the flour, bread soda and cinnamon into a separate bowl and stir in the sugar. Add the dry ingredients to the buttermilk mixture, and quickly fold in until just combined, being careful not to over-mix. Spoon into the paper cases and bake for 15-20 minutes until well risen and golden.

Leave the muffins to cool in the tin for 5 minutes, then serve while still warm.

typical nutritional content – *per portion*			
Energy Kcal (Calories)	152	Salt (g)	0.3
Fat (g)	5.5	Sugars (g)	15.8
of which saturates (g)	0.8		

irish tea brack

There are many versions of this traditional tea brack but the principles are always the same: dried fruits soaked in tea overnight and mixed with flour and an egg. It is normally served with butter but as this recipe is so moist it really isn't necessary. It keeps well wrapped in clingfilm and tinfoil.

Preparation time: 10 mins • **Cooking time:** 1 hr 30 mins + 30 mins cooling

Makes 12-16 slices

what you need

100g (4oz) sultanas
100g (4oz) currants or raisins
50g (2oz) glacé cherries, chopped
50g (2oz) cut mixed peel
1 tablespoon Irish whiskey (optional)
300ml (½ pint) strong hot tea

225g (8oz) light brown sugar
a little sunflower oil, for greasing
275g (10oz) self-raising flour
good pinch of freshly ground nutmeg
1 egg, beaten
1 tablespoon clear honey

what you do

Place the sultanas in a large bowl with the currants or raisins, glacé cherries, mixed peel and whiskey (if using). Pour the tea over the mixture and then stir in the sugar until dissolved. Cover with a plate and leave overnight to allow all the fruit to plump up.

Preheat the oven to 150°C/300°F/Gas Mark 2. Lightly grease a 1.2 litre (2 pint) non-stick loaf tin with sunflower oil and then line the base with non-stick parchment paper.

Sieve the flour and nutmeg into a bowl and then stir into the soaked fruit mixture with the egg until evenly combined.

Turn into the prepared tin and level the surface. Bake for 1½ hours or until well risen and firm to the touch. A fine skewer inserted into the centre should come out clean.

Allow the tea brack to cool in the tin for about 10 minutes before turning out. Brush the top with the honey and then leave to cool completely on a wire rack.

Slice the brack and arrange on a serving plate and allow people to help themselves.

typical nutritional content – *per portion*			
Energy Kcal (Calories)	167	Salt (g)	0.2
Fat (g)	0.7	Sugars (g)	27.9
of which saturates (g)	0.2		

mixed berry muffins

Muffins are an American invention that we have embraced and when you make your own it is easy to see why! The trick to fluffy muffins is to fold the wet and dry ingredients together as quickly as possible until just combined; don't worry if the mixture still looks a little lumpy. These muffins are best served on the day that they are made.

Preparation time: 10 mins • Cooking time: 25 mins + 5 mins cooling

Makes 10

what you need

150g (5oz) plain flour
1½ teaspoons baking powder
pinch of salt
50g (2oz) butter, at room temperature
75g (3oz) caster sugar
1 egg, lightly beaten

½ teaspoon finely grated lemon rind
150ml (¼ pint) buttermilk
100g (4oz) mixed berries, such as raspberries, blueberries and small blackberries

what you do

Preheat the oven to 180°C/350°F/Gas Mark 4. Line a muffin tin with 10 deep paper cases.

Sift the flour into a large bowl with the baking powder and salt.

Cream together the butter and sugar in a separate bowl until light and fluffy, then beat in the egg and lemon rind.

Make a well in the centre of the dry ingredients and pour in the buttermilk. Add the butter and sugar mixture and the berries and quickly mix everything together with a large metal spoon until just combined. Don't overwork the batter.

Heap the mixture into the paper cases, filling them about two-thirds full. Bake for 20 minutes until well risen and golden brown. Transfer to a wire rack. Serve warm.

variations

Cherry love
Use 75g (3oz) of dried pitted cherries instead of the mixed berries.

Blueberry and lime
Use 75g (3oz) of dried blueberries instead of the mixed berries and try lime rind instead of lemon.

Sultana and lemon
Omit the mixed berries and replace with sultanas.

typical nutritional content – *per portion* *(basic recipe)*			
Energy Kcal (Calories)	133	Salt (g)	0.4
Fat (g)	4.9	Sugars (g)	9.3
of which saturates (g)	2.8		

sponge cake with strawberries

This cake is a wonderfully indulgent dessert, perfect for a teatime treat or as a dinner party finale. It is best eaten just cooled and not long out of the oven, which is just as well as it doesn't tend to hang around for long.

Preparation time: 15 mins • **Cooking time:** 25 mins + 20 mins cooling

Serves 8

what you need

5 eggs, at room temperature
150g (5oz) caster sugar
175g (6oz) self-raising flour, sifted
finely grated rind of 1 lemon

200g (7oz) half-fat crème fraîche
225g (8oz) strawberries, hulled and sliced
½ teaspoon sifted icing sugar

what you do

Preheat the oven to 190°C/375°F/Gas Mark 5.

Place the eggs and sugar in a large bowl and, using either a hand or electric whisk, beat the mixture until it expands, filling over half the bowl, and has the consistency of lightly whipped cream.

Using a large metal spoon, gently fold in the sifted flour and continue folding until all the flour is fully absorbed, then fold in the lemon rind. Line the bases of two 20cm (8in) non-stick sandwich cake tins with non-stick parchment paper and divide the mixture between them. Cook for 20-25 minutes. When the cakes are cooked they come slightly away from the tin. Turn out onto wire racks, peel away the parchment paper and leave to cool completely.

When the cakes have cooled and you are ready to serve, beat the crème fraîche until smooth and then spread two-thirds over one of the sandwich halves. Add half of the sliced strawberries and dust lightly with icing sugar. Sandwich the two halves together and spread the rest of the crème fraîche over the top. Arrange the rest of the strawberries on the crème fraîche and dust lightly with the icing sugar. Cut into wedges and arrange on plates to serve.

typical nutritional content – *per portion*			
Energy Kcal (Calories)	240	Salt (g)	0.4
Fat (g)	7.5	Sugars (g)	22.4
of which saturates (g)	3.5		

cranberry and orange scones

If you haven't got buttermilk use ordinary milk with a good squeeze of lemon juice. Whatever you decide to use it is important to add all of the liquid at once. Otherwise you'll end up handling the dough too much which will result in the scones not being as light as they could be. Experiment with other dried fruits such as blueberries, cherries or mango.

Preparation time: 10 mins • **Cooking time:** 20 mins + 20 mins cooling • *Makes 8*

what you need

225g (8oz) self-raising flour, plus extra for dusting
pinch of salt
1 teaspoon bread soda or baking powder
40g (1½oz) butter

50g (2oz) dried cranberries
finely grated rind of 1 orange
about 150ml (¼ pint) buttermilk
beaten egg, to glaze

what you do

Preheat the oven to 220°C/425°F/Gas Mark 7.

Sift the flour, salt and bread soda or baking powder into a bowl. Rub in the butter until the mixture resembles fine breadcrumbs. Fold in the dried cranberries and orange rind and then gradually stir in enough buttermilk to give a fairly soft, light dough.

On a lightly floured surface, lightly roll out the dough to a 2cm (¾in) thickness and cut into rounds with a 6cm (2½in) cutter (if you don't have a cutter you could use a glass).

Place on a non-stick baking sheet and brush the tops liberally with the beaten egg. Bake for 10-12 minutes until well risen and golden brown. Place on a wire rack. Serve while still warm.

variations

Pear and almond

Omit the dried cranberries and add 50g (2oz) ready-to-eat dried pears, chopped, and 25g (1oz) of toasted chopped almonds instead of the orange rind.

Apple

Omit the dried cranberries and orange rind and add one eating apple which has been peeled, cored and finely chopped, and also put in a pinch of ground mixed spice.

typical nutritional content – *per portion* *(basic recipe)*			
Energy Kcal (Calories)	239	Salt (g)	1.0
Fat (g)	5.5	Sugars (g)	1.9
of which saturates (g)	3.0		

date and walnut loaf

This is a very dark bread and keeps extremely well when wrapped in clingfilm and tinfoil. The dates give it an extra sweetness and make it a tasty treat.

Preparation time: 15 mins + 5 mins resting • **Cooking time:** 1 hr + 30 mins cooling

Makes about 16 slices

what you need

50g (2oz) butter
a little oil for greasing
200g (7oz) wholemeal flour, plus extra for dusting
150g (5oz) plain flour
1 teaspoon bread soda
100g (4oz) light brown sugar

100g (4oz) dates, finely chopped
50g (2oz) walnuts, shelled and chopped
1 large egg
225ml (8fl oz) buttermilk
1 tablespoon clear honey or treacle

what you do

Preheat the oven to 160°C/325°F/Gas Mark 3.

Melt the butter in a small pan or in the microwave. Set aside to cool a little. Lightly oil a 1.2 litre (2 pint) loaf tin and dust with flour.

Sift the wholemeal and plain flour into a bowl with the bread soda, tipping in any remaining bran flakes that are left in the bottom of the sieve. Stir in the sugar and then fold in the dates and walnuts.

In a separate jug, beat together the egg, buttermilk and honey or treacle. Make a well in the centre of the dry ingredients and then pour in the egg mixture followed by the cooled melted butter. Quickly mix to a smooth batter and transfer to the prepared loaf tin.

Place in the oven and bake for 1 hour or until golden brown and a skewer stuck into the middle of the loaf comes out clean.

Once the loaf is cooked, leave it to settle in the tin for 5 minutes, then turn out onto a wire rack and leave to cool completely.

Cut into slices and arrange on a serving plate.

typical nutritional content – *per portion*			
Energy Kcal (Calories)	169	Salt (g)	0.3
Fat (g)	5.6	Sugars (g)	13.0
of which saturates (g)	2.0		

oatmeal and apricot cookies

These delicious soft cookies are a perfect treat. Feel free to replace the apricots with any ready-to-eat dried fruit such as peach, pineapple or mango. Of course, raisins would also work well. These cookies have the added benefit of freezing very well and defrost in minutes when needed.

Preparation time: 15 mins + 2 mins resting • **Cooking time:** 15 mins + 10 mins cooling

Makes about 40

what you need

100g (4oz) butter, at room temperature
175g (6oz) light brown sugar
2 eggs, lightly beaten
150g (5oz) wholemeal flour
150g (5oz) plain flour
1 teaspoon bread soda

150g (5oz) oatmeal
75g (3oz) ready-to-eat dried apricots, finely chopped
2-3 tablespoons low-fat milk
4 tablespoons flaked almonds

what you do

Preheat the oven to 180°C/350°F/Gas Mark 4.

Place the butter and sugar in a large bowl and, using a hand-held beater or wooden spoon, cream together until light and fluffy. Slowly add in the eggs until evenly combined.

Sieve the wholemeal and plain flour into a separate bowl with the bread soda, then add to the butter mixture and gently fold in. Finally fold in the oatmeal and apricots, adding enough of the milk to stop the mixture from becoming too dry and difficult to mix.

Form into walnut-sized balls and arrange on large non-stick sturdy baking sheets, well spaced apart to allow some room for expansion. Sprinkle each cookie with a few flaked almonds and then gently flatten with a fork or your hand. Bake for 12-15 minutes until cooked through and lightly golden.

Leave the cookies to settle for a couple of minutes on the baking sheets and then transfer to a wire rack and leave to cool completely. Stack the cookies up on a plate to serve.

typical nutritional content – *per portion*			
Energy Kcal (Calories)	82	Salt (g)	0.1
Fat (g)	3.1	Sugars (g)	5.1
of which saturates (g)	1.4		

carrot cake with rosemary cream

The orange rind and seasoning make for a wonderfully aromatic taste and the walnuts really enhance the texture of this fabulously indulgent cake. This is perfect as a treat with a nice cup of tea.

Preparation time: 15 mins • **Cooking time:** 1 hr 30 mins + 30 mins cooling • *Serves 8-10*

what you need

For the carrot cake
150ml (¼ pint) sunflower oil
2 eggs
175g (6oz) light brown sugar
finely grated rind of 1 orange
225g (8oz) carrots, coarsely grated
50g (2oz) shelled walnuts, chopped
50g (2oz) raisins
175g (6oz) self-raising flour
1 teaspoon baking powder

½ teaspoon ground cinnamon
pinch of ground nutmeg

For the rosemary cream
juice of 1 orange
1 tablespoon caster sugar
1 small fresh rosemary sprig
200g (7oz) carton half-fat crème fraîche

what you do

Preheat the oven to 160°C/325°F/Gas Mark 3. Line a 1.2 litre (2 pint) non-stick loaf tin with non-stick parchment paper.

Place the oil in a food processor with the eggs, sugar and orange rind, then blend until well combined. Place the carrots, walnuts and raisins in a large bowl and, using a large metal spoon, fold in the oil mixture.

Sift the flour on top of the carrot mixture with the baking powder, cinnamon and nutmeg, then fold in until just combined. Pour into the prepared tin and bake for 1¼–1½ hours or until well risen and firm to the touch. If in doubt, a fine skewer should come out clean when inserted in the middle.

Meanwhile, make the rosemary cream. Place the orange juice in a small pan with the caster sugar and rosemary, then simmer until reduced in volume by half. Remove from the heat, and allow to cool completely, then remove the rosemary sprig and discard. Fold into the crème fraîche, then cover and chill until ready to use.

Leave the cooked carrot cake to cool in the tin for about 5 minutes, then transfer on to a wire rack to cool completely, gently peeling off the parchment paper.

To serve, cut the carrot cake into slices and arrange on plates with a dollop of the rosemary cream.

typical nutritional content – *per portion*			
Energy Kcal (Calories)	357	Salt (g)	0.3
Fat (g)	21.5	Sugars (g)	26.2
of which saturates (g)	4.3		

Use the Food Pyramid to plan your healthy food choices every day and watch your portion size

HEALTH PROMOTION UNIT
DEPARTMENT OF HEALTH AND CHILDREN
www.healthpromotion.ie

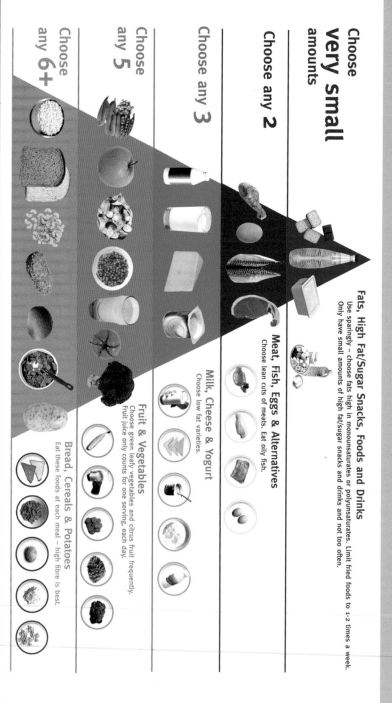

Choose very small amounts

Fats, High Fat/Sugar Snacks, Foods and Drinks
Use sparingly – choose fats high in monounsaturates or polyunsaturates. Limit fried foods to 1-2 times a week. Only have small amounts of high fat/sugar snacks and drinks and not too often.

Choose any 2

Meat, Fish, Eggs & Alternatives
Choose lean cuts of meats. Eat oily fish.

Choose any 3

Milk, Cheese & Yogurt
Choose low fat varieties.

Choose any 5

Fruit & Vegetables
Choose green leafy vegetables and citrus fruit frequently. Fruit juice only counts for one serving, each day.

Choose any 6+

Bread, Cereals & Potatoes
Eat these foods at each meal – high fibre is best.

Drink water regularly - at least 8 cups a day

FOLIC ACID - AN ESSENTIAL INGREDIENT IN MAKING A BABY. YOU CAN GET FOLIC ACID FROM GREEN LEAFY VEGETABLES BUT IF THERE IS ANY POSSIBILITY THAT YOU COULD BECOME PREGNANT THEN YOU SHOULD BE TAKING A FOLIC ACID TABLET (400 MICROGRAMS PER DAY).